Song Birds

OF THE WORLD

by Oliver L. Austin, Jr.

Florida State Museum, University of Florida

ILLUSTRATED BY ARTHUR SINGER

EDITED BY HERBERT S. ZIM

GOLDEN PRESS • NEW YORK

ABOUT THE AUTHOR: Dr. Oliver L. Austin, Jr., is curator of birds at the Florida State Museum. He has done extensive field work not only in North America but also in the Antarctic, Korea, New Zealand, the South Pacific, and Central America, and has probably banded more birds than anyone else in the world. He has published innumerable papers and articles, and has written two definitive books, *Birds of Korea* and *Birds of Japan*.

ABOUT THE ILLUSTRATOR: Arthur Singer studied at Cooper Union Art School and is the first recipient of its medal for distinguished work. His painstaking attention to detail, his masterly technique, and his eye for design have won him general recognition as one of the foremost painters of birds in the world today.

ABOUT THE EDITOR: Dr. Herbert S. Zim is a noted authority on science education, and the author and editor of many books on science and nature.

Contents

INTRODUCTION

This volume deals with the tremendous galaxy of song and perching birds that scientists call the passerines and place at the top of the avian family tree in the order Passeriformes. Among them are many of the world's commonest and most familiar birds. Here are the lowly sparrows and buntings of man's dooryards and roadsides, the confiding swallows that nest under the eaves of his dwellings, the friendly titmice, thrushes, and warblers of his gardens and orchards, and the larks and pipits of his cultivated fields. Here are the canaries he has bred for their song and brought indoors to fill his home with melody. Here are the great imitators—the mockingbirds of the New World, the mynas of the Old, and the greatest mimics of all, the lyrebirds of Australia. Here are the House Sparrow and Common Starling that man has introduced from their native Europe to his settlements the world around.

The passerines are land birds, and they occur on all the major land areas of the world except Antarctica, and on all but the most remote and barren of the oceanic islands as well. In most lands they are the dominant bird group. Representatives have radiated out to fill all possible habitats except the most inhospitable. They live successfully from the lush forests of the tropics to the treeless tundras of the Arctic. They manage to survive wherever food and shelter are obtainable on rugged mountainsides and in the great deserts. They have learned to endure subzero cold and baking tropical heat, and to subsist on a wide range of animal and vegetable foods.

A number have become dependent on moist environments in marshes or next to fresh-water streams and lakes—the mudlarks, wagtails, marsh wrens, and reed warblers come immediately to mind. Others, such as the shore larks and the rock thrushes, find the sea beaches to their liking on occasion. Only one small family, the four species of dippers, has accustomed itself to living in a predominantly aqueous habitat.

Some groups, such as the crows and the thrushes, are of widespread, almost cosmopolitan distribution. Others, such as the Eurasian accentors, the Hawaiian honeycreepers, and the New Zealand wattlebirds, are limited to one or two particular geographical regions. Still others, such as the Dusky and Cape Sable Seaside sparrows, are extremely sedentary and spend their entire lives, generation after generation, within a few acres of specialized habitat.

A complex and highly varied aggregation, the Passeriformes number about 5,150 species, or roughly three-fifths of the world's 8,655 known living birds. We divide them among 57, or slightly more than one-third of the world's generally recognized 160 bird families. Their outstanding anatomical feature is their perching feet, with four toes joined at the same level, three in front and one behind. The hind toe is usually the strongest and the best developed, and it is never reversible.

In its simplest form the passerine foot is an ideal mechanism for grasping a small perch and supporting the owner firmly on it. The activating muscles and tendons are so contrived that the grasp tightens if the bird tends to fall backward. Nevertheless the foot is broadly adaptable, and it serves a number of other uses. It is an efficient organ for walking, running, or hopping on flat ground, where the larks, pipits, pittas, tapaculos, and some icterids spend most if not all their lives. It serves the woodcreepers, nuthatches, and tree creepers admirably for clinging to bark and climbing woodpecker-fashion around tree trunks. The toes are never webbed, even in the stream-inhabiting dippers.

Other characteristics that set the Passeriformes apart from

the members of the other 28 orders of birds are the peculiar structure of their palate bones, their short necks with the cervical vertebrae reduced usually to 14 or 13 (15 in the broadbills alone), and a distinctive type of spermatozoa. Of particular significance is their highly developed voice box, or syrinx, which is responsible for the presence among them of the best vocalists and mimics in the animal kingdom.

In most other aspects the passerines vary greatly. In size they range from the tiny kinglets, wrens, and gnatcatchers to the moderately large ravens and lyrebirds. In colors they run from the black crows and drongos and the almost white cotingas through miscellaneous drab grays and browns to the gaudy orioles and tanagers and the brilliantly iridescent sunbirds. The feathers of most are plain and utilitarian with little embellishment, but the birds of paradise carry the development of ornate plumages to its acme among birds.

The form of the bill shows a wide adaptation to gathering a diversity of foods. Most generalized are the comparatively softish, rounded bills of the crows, jays, thrushes, and warblers, useful for gathering both animal and vegetable food. Among the specialized types are the hard, conical bills of the seedeaters, the sharply-hooked raptorine bills of the shrikes, the short bills of the swallows masking their wide gape for taking insects in flight, the slender down-curved tubes of the honey creepers and sunbirds for gathering nectar, and the thin, pointed, chisel-like tweezers of the nuthatchs and creepers for prying into bark crevices.

Although all have altricial young that hatch blind, helpless, naked or nearly so, and are reared in the nest, the passerines' breeding habits also vary considerably. Most lay clutches of 2 to 5 eggs; the largest are the 12- to 14-egg clutches of some of the titmice. Only the lyrebirds are known definitely to lay but a single egg at each nesting. Types of nests vary from simple, crudely-lined scrapes in the ground or masses of twigs or grass stuffed into a natural cavity, through a gamut of open or covered structures of varying materials, workmanship, and complexity at all heights in all types of vegetation, to the complicated communal apartment dwellings of the Palm Chat and certain weavers.

The ancestry of the passerines and the relationships to other orders of land birds are an enigma. Only recently have paleo-ornithologists begun to sift fossil-bearing deposits for tiny bird bones that are now yielding a few clues to the pre-Ice Age distribution and relationships of a few passerine families. The passerines probably arose very early in Tertiary time, or perhaps earlier, from several parent stocks. The few early Tertiary remains are too fragmentary to be identified with certainty, and they offer no clues·as yet to the perplexing questions of the perching birds' antecedents.

During and since Tertiary time, the passerines have evolved more rapidly and successfully than any other avian order. So rapid and so recent has their development been that the lines of demarcation between many groups are not yet well defined. The differences between some passerine families are not so great as those between many non-passerine genera. This, and the persistence of primitive forms that do not manifestly link more highly developed stocks, make subdividing the order into more "manageable" families most difficult.

Ornithologists are by no means as yet agreed on the exact delineation of the passerine families. Only one proposal to subdivide the order into major groups has stood the test of time. More than a century ago the German anatomist, Johannes Müller, pointed out basic differences in the number and attachment of the muscles of the syrinx that permit the recognition of four suborders. The first three suborders, with 3 or 4 pairs of syrinx muscles, are the primitive passerines, the so-called "suboscines." The first of these is the suborder Eurylaimi with the single Old World family of broadbills. Next is the suborder Tyranni, a group of 12 families that includes the New World tyrant flycatchers, ovenbirds, antbirds, cotingas, and their kin, and the Old World pittas, New Zealand wrens, and Madagascar asities of highly uncertain origin and kinship. Third is the Menurae, containing only the two lyrebirds and the two scrub-birds of Australia.

The fourth suborder, the Passeres or "true oscines," have 5 to 8 pairs of syrinx muscles. This large aggregation of true singing birds contains slightly more than 4,100 species, almost half of the world's birds. Students now divide it into from 36 to 55 or more families. Efforts to unite these families into larger natural groups have met with little success or accord, and the sequence in which they are listed is still a matter of contention between various schools of thought.

Most Europeans put the crows at the apex of the family tree. This seems largely a matter of custom, defended on the debatable grounds of the crows' alleged high intelligence. Near them they place the birds of paradise and bower-birds for their complex and highly specialized development of plumages and behavior patterns. The American school of thought places the seedeaters and the related nine-primaried oscines in the top position. These show the greatest and most recent adaptive radiation and development. They are today the dominant and most successful of all bird groups. Many ornithologists, myself among them, feel they represent the main stream of modern songbird evolution.

The material has been taken from my "BIRDS OF THE WORLD" (Golden Press, 1961) which treats of all the major bird families. This book incorporates most of the essential art of the original, and the text has been revised to include new material based on recent taxonomic researches and other developments of ornithological importance during the past six years.

Here then, are the "song birds," and I hope you will find in them as much enjoyment as they have and still continue to give me.

Gainesville, Florida.   Oliver Austin, Jr.
March, 1967

BROADBILLS

PASSERIFORMES   EURYLAIMIDAE

The 14 species of broadbills are a distinctive family of bright-colored perching birds distributed erratically in the Old World tropics. Their simple syrinx controlled by a single pair of muscles, the partial joining of their front toes, and their 15 (instead of 14) neck vertebrae set them so apart from all other passerines they are placed in a separate suborder. Their primitiveness and disjointed distribution suggest the living broadbills are the remnants of an ancient group that was once of wider distribution and is now past its peak of development. Their relationships are uncertain, but they seem closest to the New World cotingas and puffbirds.

Chunky birds from 5 to 11 inches in length, the broadbills have disproportionately large heads set on short necks and, as their name implies, heavy, wide, flattened bills hooked at the tip. Their short legs add to their squat appearance, but their feet are strong and their toes are tipped with long curved claws. Their soft, silky plumage is brightly colored green and blue in most Asiatic species; the African forms are more somber but relieved with gay patches of red, yellow, and lavender. Their bills and large eyes are often a vivid hue. Females are usually duller than the males.

The family is divided into two subfamilies, the typical broadbills (Eurylaiminae) and the green broadbills (Calyptomeninae). The typical broadbills are uncrested and have 11 primaries, and graduated or rounded tails. Seven species of five genera range across southeastern Asia from the Himalayas to the Philippines and southward to Sumatra and Borneo. Four species are limited to the forests of central and southern Africa. The single genus of green broadbills is found only in the oriental region. Its three species have 10 primaries, short, square tails, and their smaller bills are partly hidden by a frontal crest of thick feathers.

All the broadbills are birds of wet jungles and cloud forests.

Some live continually near the ground; others inhabit the treetops. Most are sedentary, and some are extremely restricted in their movements. Two of the green broadbills, the rare Magnificent and the Black-throated, are found only in the mountain forests of northern Borneo. Rarest of all is Grauer's Broadbill, of which fewer than a dozen specimens are known, all taken in a small tract of bamboo forest in the mountains near Lake Tanganyika. It is a tiny greenish bird, scarcely 5 inches long, with a blue throat and breast. It apparently lives in the treetops and catches insects in flight.

Commoner and better known is the Long-tailed Broadbill, widespread from the Himalayan foothills through southeast Asia to Sumatra and Borneo. These chunky birds work through the jungles in small flocks, climbing through the lianas in parrot fashion in search of insects, chattering continually to one another. They are remarkably tame and unsuspicious, even failing to take alarm when some of the flock are shot.

The typical broadbills are insectivorous, and also take occasional small frogs and lizards. They find much of their food on foliage and catch flying insects on the wing. The green broadbills, of which the Lesser Green Broadbill of Malaya is the most widespread and best known, live largely on fruit and berries. They are rather solitary, silent birds.

Broadbills have superlative skill at nest building. They weave a long, hanging, purselike structure of grasses, rootlets, and other fibers, tapered gracefully at top and bottom. This they suspend by a slender string, woven of the same materials, from a branch or vine in the forest, often over a stream or pool. The nest proper in the center is entered through a hole in the side which may have a sheltering portico and doorstep perch.

Within this intricate nest the broadbills lay from 2 to 8 (usually 3 to 5) white or buffy eggs, sometimes spotted around the larger end. Beyond these few facts little is known of their breeding habits. Both sexes have been observed building the nest, and for the Dusky Broadbill of Thailand there is evi-

LESSER GREEN BROADBILL
Calyptomena viridis
Malaya, Sumatra, Borneo   6 in.

LONG-TAILED BROADBILL
Psarisomus dalhousiae
Himalayas to Indochina, Sumatra, Borneo   10 in.

dence that as many as 10 birds may work on the same nest. Both sexes have been seen bringing food to the young, but whether they share incubation duties is unknown, as is the length of the incubation period.

Several broadbills have specialized courtship displays involving the sudden flashing of bright patches of feathers on the back, usually concealed under the wings. The Red-sided Broadbill of Africa, which the Congo natives call the "cock of the forest" because it is the first bird to greet the breaking day, makes sudden short display flights in which the bird flits in a small circle a foot or two in diameter above its perch with a trilling froglike croak made by the vibrating stiff wing feathers.

WOODCREEPERS

PASSERIFORMES   DENDROCOLAPTIDAE

Strongly resembling the familiar Brown Creeper of northern woodlands in appearance and actions, though usually somewhat larger and darker, are 47 species of slender, brownish birds found in American tropical and subtropical forests from Mexico to northern Argentina. These are the woodcreepers, a well-marked family of very similar birds in no way related to the true oscine creepers, but belonging to the more primitive suborder Tyranni, whose members have much simpler vocal organs. The woodcreepers' closest relatives are the ovenbirds, with which they share such structural characteristics as two pairs of syrinx muscles and partially joined front toes. Some students classify the woodcreepers and the ovenbirds as subfamilies of the same family.

The woodcreepers' superficial resemblance to the oscine creepers is a fine example of parallel evolution in widely separate stocks which have similar needs in comparable ecological niches in their respective parts of the world. Both live chiefly on the trunks of forest trees, clinging to the bark with their sharply curved toenails and propping themselves upright, woodpecker fashion, with their stiff, spiny tails.

The woodcreepers are not shy birds, but are so protectively colored they are hard to observe. All are dull brown with ruddy brown wing and tail feathers. A few, such as the Olivaceous and Ruddy woodcreepers of Central America, are plain immaculate browns. Most species, however, have the head, back, and underparts variously streaked, mottled, or barred with black, buff, gray, or white. Though their patterns are distinctive enough, they are hard to discern at a distance, especially against the birds' usual background of brown bark. Easier field marks are the relative sizes of the different species, and the length and shape of their bills.

RED-BILLED SCYTHEBILL
Campyloramphus trochilirostris
Panama to Argentina 9 in.

BARRED WOODCREEPER
Dendrocolaptes certhia
Mexico to Brazil 11 in.

OLIVACEOUS WOODCREEPER
Sittasomus griseicapillus
Mexico to Argentina 6½ in.

Woodcreepers vary in length from 5½ to 14 inches. Their laterally compressed bills range from short and straight to long and sharply down-curved—adaptations for searching bark crannies, probing into mosses, ferns, and epiphytes, or for picking grubs out of their burrows. Their beaks are not the strong chisels of the woodpeckers and are used essentially as probes. Most woodcreepers work methodically when feeding. Starting near the base of a tree, they move spirally upward, searching each crack and fissure. A few species feed occasionally on the ground, working over fallen logs.

Woodcreepers usually travel about singly or in pairs. Often one or two are found among the mixed flocks of antbirds, flycatchers, and tanagers that move irregularly through the rainforests. None is migratory, but individuals wander considerably. They fly strongly, but only from tree to tree.

Woodcreepers are quite vocal and their simple repetitive calls are commonly heard in the tropical American forests. Their range of expression is limited by the primitive structure of their sound-producing organs. The calls may be flutey trills or loud, harsh nasal notes. Some woodcreepers rap with their bills on hollow stubs in woodpecker fashion as part of their courtship, but their tapping does not have regular cadences.

Woodcreepers are cavity nesters, but as their beaks are not strong enough to chisel into wood, they use natural hollows in rotten stubs or take over those abandoned by woodpeckers. They tend to pick sites with very small entrances, barely large enough for passage. Some remove chips or trash from the hole and use it bare. Others make a crude pad of bark flakes or dead leaves, which they renew constantly through the nesting period, a habit shared by the related ovenbirds.

The normal clutch is 2 to 3 white eggs, sometimes with a greenish tinge, always unspotted and rounded at both ends. Both sexes incubate, and they relieve each other frequently through the day. The incubation period averages about 15 days. The young hatch naked except for a slight fuzz on the back and remain in the nest about 3 weeks. Their parents continue to feed them several weeks after they leave the nest.

OVENBIRDS

PASSERIFORMES   FURNARIIDAE

The ovenbirds are a large family of primitive passerines noted for their extremely varied nesting habits and named for the intricate clay nests, shaped like an old-fashioned Dutch oven, a few build. Found from southern Mexico to Patagonia, the family has its greatest development and diversity in southern South America. The familiar North American Ovenbird is not a member of this family, but a wood warbler.

The 217 species in the ovenbird family are small to medium in size, 5 to 11 inches long. Most are plain, brownish above and lighter below, often with contrasting white throats. Some are spotted or streaked with black, white, or rufous,

STRIATED EARTH-CREEPER
Upucerthia serrana
Peruvian Andes   8 in.

and only a few have distinctive color patterns. The sexes are alike or nearly so. Ovenbirds differ from the closely allied woodcreepers in having elongated instead of round nostrils. Their front toes are not joined together as far, and their outer toes are not distinctly larger than the inner.

Though predominantly forest birds, the ovenbirds have a wide range of habitats. A few occupy coastal sand dunes, many live on the open pampas and adjoining brushlands, and others dwell at considerable altitudes above the tree line in the Andes. All are insect eaters, but a few eat some seeds and vegetable matter. One group, the treerunners, climb tree trunks and brace themselves with their tails like the wood-creepers. Another, the foliage-gleaners, forage among the leaves and branches. The leafscrapers turn over the detritus on the jungle floor. One small group, the spinetails, is made up of marsh inhabitants that look and behave like large marsh wrens. The shaketails live along watercourses and wag their tails continually the way dippers, wagtails, and many other stream-loving birds do. But most ovenbirds feed on the ground and act more like larks or thrushes.

So far as known both sexes share the nesting duties. Oven-birds lay from 2 to 6 eggs, usually white (pale bluish in one group) and unmarked. Incubation varies from 2 to 3 weeks, and the young usually remain in the nest from 12 to 18 days. They show great variety in their choice of nesting sites and type of nest. About the only type of nest they do not seem to build is the simple open cup.

Many terrestrial ovenbirds dig nest tunnels in the earth. One group, the miners, excavates burrows 5 to 10 feet into a bank, ending in a round chamber which the birds line with soft grasses. Other tunnel nesters include the foliage-gleaners of the genera *Automolus* and *Philydor,* and the little whiskered *Xenops,* one of the smallest members of the family, with a strangely up-curved bill. The terrestrial shake-tails and the earthcreepers shelter their nests in rock crannies, and some build in natural cavities in trees and stumps.

The widespread spinetails build complex covered structures

of twigs and grasses, sometimes on or near the ground, sometimes high in trees. The castle-builders and firewood-gatherers build bulky nests of sticks that seem too big for these 6- to 8-inch birds to carry. The Red-fronted Thornbill builds a huge columnar, communal nest, usually around a bare branch high above the ground. Four or five pairs build the castle

WHITE-CHEEKED SPINETAIL
Schoeniophylax phryganophila
Brazil to Argentina   7½ in.

RUFOUS OVENBIRD
Furnarius rufus
Southern Brazil and Argentina   8 in.

PALE-BREASTED SPINETAIL
Synallaxis albescens
Costa Rica to Argentina   5½ in.

PLAIN XENOPS
Xenops minutus
Mexico to Brazil
and Paraguay

together, and each occupies a separate compartment within it. Other spinetails make rounded twig nests with pipelike entrances at one side; some have complex entrances leading downward from the top. Still another group, the marsh inhabitants, builds domed nests of reeds plastered with mud.

Best known, and largely responsible for the family name, is the Rufous Ovenbird of southern Brazil, Paraguay, and Argentina, which Spanish Americans call *el hornero,* the baker. The baker is a drab 8-inch bird, rather thrushlike in aspect, that prefers open country. It is plentiful around houses and along roadsides. It walks about conspicuously in the open, but takes shelter in trees when disturbed.

The baker nests during the rainy season, from December to February, when mud is plentiful. Its domed, ovenlike nests, usually about 12 inches long, 8 inches wide, and 10 inches high, are built of mud reinforced with grass and straw. The entrance hole near the bottom is separated from the nest chamber by an inner spiral threshold. The birds build these nests in the open on fence posts, bare limbs, and often on the eaves of houses. Strong and durable, the nests last for several years, and are often appropriated by swallows and other cavity nesters. The bakers build new nests each year.

ANTBIRDS

PASSERIFORMES   FORMICARIIDAE

Another tremendous family of primitive passerine birds limited in range to continental Central and South America is the bewildering array of antbirds. The family numbers 230 species divided among some 50 genera that range through the forests and scrublands from southern Mexico to Paraguay and northern Argentina. Their center of abundance is in the rainforest jungles of the vast Amazon drainage.

Like the ovenbirds, to which they seem most nearly related, the antbirds are small- to medium-sized birds ranging from 4 to 14 inches in length. They are rather dull-colored and patterned inconspicuously, for the most part in drab browns, russets, grays, and blacks. Their front toes are slightly joined at the base, and their plumage is rather loose-webbed. Antbirds differ from the ovenbirds structurally in the manner of the scaling of their legs, and in having their beaks always hooked at the tip, strongly so in some genera. Also, male and female antbirds are usually unlike in color, often markedly so, and their nest construction is simpler and more uniform. A few antbirds build covered nests on the ground, a few line tree cavities, but most make open cup nests, occasionally on the ground, more often between the forks of a low branch.

Antbirds are largely forest dwellers, and most of them haunt the dark lower strata on or near the jungle floor, where, as their name implies, most are fairly intimately associated with ants. Some species, notably the antcatchers, live largely on ants and termites, but most antbirds follow the wandering columns of ants to feed on the insects and other small life the ants disturb. As the files of voracious army ants move inexorably through the jungle, everything able to move gets out of their way in a mad scramble for safety, throwing caution to the winds as though fleeing a forest fire. This makes very good hunting indeed for all avian insectivores, and the antbirds make a special practice of taking advantage of it. Individual antbirds of several species can usually be found harrowing the flanks of an active phalanx of army ants.

These loose bands that follow an ant column seldom contain more than one or two antbirds of any one species, for the antbirds are not as a rule gregarious. I have seen as many as six White-plumed Antbirds hunting together in the Guiana forests, but these birds may have been a family group which had not yet separated. This startlingly crested species, however, is reported to move about in small, tight flocks. Antbirds are weak fliers and none is migratory.

Few of the antbirds are conspicuous or distinctive enough to have earned well-established common names and, except for the commonest and best-known species, the names that have been manufactured for them have yet to be confirmed by usage. The more distinctive groups of antbirds are generally distinguished by the names of the types of birds they seem to resemble. The smallest of the antbirds, for instance, are commonly called antwrens, though to me they are wrenlike only in size. The antwrens do scurry through the underbrush and are hard to see, but otherwise they are not wrenlike in either appearance or actions.

A more aptly named group is the antvireos, slightly larger birds, 5 to 7 inches long, that work the lower branches of trees in vireo fashion and build vireo-like nests suspended between forked branches. A group of still larger species that feed both on the ground and in the brushy understory are called antthrushes. Other fairly well-marked groups are the antcreepers, antshrikes, and antpittas. Those that fit into none of these handy categories retain the collective family name of antbird. One small genus of Brazilian antbirds with unfeathered facial patches is justly called the bare-eyes, and another with bright irides is known as the fire-eyes.

The antpittas are so distinctive they are sometimes given subfamily rank. These are chunky birds often the size of a quail or larger, with comparatively long legs, noticeably large heads, and short stubby tails. Like the Old World pittas, which they strongly resemble in everything but color, the antpittas are shy, retiring birds of the forest floor and hard to observe. They have loud voices, and pairs are given to the common antbird habit of calling back and forth antiphonally to one another.

For birds with such primitive vocal organs—some have only a single pair of syrinx muscles—the antbirds are surprisingly vocal. Their calls are so distinctive that they are often more easily recognized than the birds themselves, which constantly stay hidden in the thick forest cover.

Perhaps the best known and most familiar of the family are the antshrikes, all of which have the bill strongly hooked and

WHITE-FLANKED ANTWREN ♂
Myrmotherula axillaris
Honduras to Brazil 4 in.

WHITE-PLUMED ANTBIRD
Pithys albifrons
Venezuela, the Guianas, Brazil 5½ in.

BARRED ANTSHRIKE ♂
Thamnophilus doliatus
Mexico to Argentina 7 in.

GREAT ANTSHRIKE ♂
Taraba major
Mexico to Argentina 8 in.

BLACK-SPOTTED BARE-EYE
Phlegopsis nigro-maculata
Central Brazil 7 in.

CHESTNUT-BACKED ANTBIRD
Myrmeciza exsul
Nicaragua to Ecuador 5½ in.

SPOTTED ANTBIRD
Hylophylax naevioides
Nicaragua to Ecuador 5½ in.

SCALED ANTPITTA
Grallaria guatimalensis
Mexico to Peru and Brazil 7½ in.

STREAK-CHESTED ANTPITTA
Grallaria perspicillata
Nicaragua to Ecuador 6½ in.

with a small tooth. All are somewhat shrikelike in their actions. One of the most widespread is the Barred Antshrike, found from Yucatan, where I first met it, southward to Bolivia. The male is strikingly barred in black and white, the female a plain dull brown. It is a noisy, active species that frequents roadside thickets and brushy tangles, and announces itself with a series of rapidly descending trilling calls. It also has quite a vocabulary of whines and chattering notes that it utters when disturbed.

The nesting habits of the Barred Antshrike have been well studied, and are apparently typical of most of the family. These birds build a simple cup nest in the branches fairly near the ground. Both sexes share all the duties of reproduction from nest building to caring for the young till they are on their own. Male and female alternate incubating at 1- to 2-hour intervals throughout the day, but the female takes the night shift alone. The normal clutch is 2 to 3 eggs, which are buffy white and lightly spotted. The incubation period is 15 to 16 days. The young hatch naked, but mature very rapidly and are usually able to leave the nest in from 8 to 11 days.

BLACK-CHEEKED GNATEATER
Conopophaga melanops
Eastern Brazil   4 in.

BLACK-BREASTED GNATEATER
Conopophaga melanogaster
Central Brazil and Bolivia   5½ in.

The antpipits, also called gnateaters (the translation of their generic name), are a poorly known group of 8 species found in the Amazon rainforests and adjoining Andes foothills. All are tiny birds, the largest only 5½ inches long, dressed in somber browns and olive greens relieved in most species by a conspicuous white line over the eye. Formerly given familial rank, they are now regarded as a subfamily of the antbirds.

Antpipits are smooth, sleek, stocky birds that, except for their small size and dull colors, resemble Old World pittas more than they do pipits. Like the pittas, they live on or close to the forest floor, and have comparatively large heads, long legs, and stout feet. Their feathers are soft and loose-webbed, those of the rump being very long and lax. Yet antpipits present a singularly well-groomed appearance, with never a feather ruffled or out of place. Short and rounded wings mark them as weak fliers. They are nonmigratory.

They differ from other antbirds in the shape of the bill which, though similarly hooked, is much broader and flattened, like that of a flycatcher. They share with the tapaculos the distinction of being the only passerine birds having the posterior end of the sternum with 4 instead of 2 notches.

While antpipits are neither overly timid or shy, they are nowhere plentiful. They live in thick, impenetrable cover where they are hard to find and even harder to observe. Their voices consist of simple, unimpressive, rather sibilant call notes. One of the best-known species, the Black-cheeked Antpipit, makes a sucking noise. The Brazilians inelegantly call it "chupadenta," the toothsucker, or "cuspidor," the spitter.

TAPACULOS

PASSERIFORMES   RHINOCRYPTIDAE

When Charles Darwin encountered one of these birds in Chile during the *Beagle's* voyage in 1834 he wrote: "It is called *Tapacolo,* or 'cover your posterior'; and well does the shameless little bird deserve its name; for it carries its tail more than erect, that is, inclined backward toward its head." The perky little birds have earned other appropriate vernacular names. Argentinians call them "gallitos," the little cocks; one Chilean species is known as "el Turco," the Turk. Alliterative names based on their distinctive calls include "huet-huet," "chucao," and "tococo" for the one Darwin wrote about.

The 27 species of tapaculos are terrestrial, nonmigratory birds of dry grassy plains and scrublands or of the thick undegrowth of montane forests. They are most numerous in the temperate southern third of South America, where they inhabit dry and barren hillsides from Tierra del Fuego northward to southern Brazil. A few species have extended the family's range at higher elevations into southern Central America. The northernmost form, the Silver-fronted Tapaculo, lives in cloud forests and wet ravines 6,000 to 10,000 feet above sea level in western Panama and Costa Rica.

Stout-bodied little birds from 4½ to 10 inches long, tapaculos have large, strong legs and feet as befits ground-living species. Their rounded wings are short and weak, and as a group they are perhaps the poorest fliers of all the passerines, with the possible exception of the New Zealand wrens. They seldom flutter more than a few yards, and escape danger by running or hopping. The flying muscles of their breasts are rather flabby and underdeveloped compared to the strong, firm thigh muscles that power their legs.

The tapaculo's plumage is soft and loose. The sexes are colored alike in somber browns and grays, often attractively barred and scalloped with reddish browns or black. Their closest relatives are the antpipits, with which they share a unique four-notched sternum, but they differ in the scaling of the tarsus, which more nearly resembles that of the antbirds. Tapaculos' nostrils are covered with a movable flap, or operculum, which may keep out dust during windstorms.

Tapaculos eat insects and some vegetable matter such as buds and seeds. Many of them scratch in the dirt or in the litter of the forest floor like chickens. They are active and inquisitive, and are experts at keeping out of sight. The brushland species, like the gallitos of Argentina, keep to shrubby cover and dart across open spaces with amazingly long strides. When surprised in the open they scurry into hiding like so many mice. The little 7-inch Brown Gallito is a fabulous runner, and takes 6-inch strides as it scurries in erratic zigzags out of the way of the intruder. Darwin described the movements of the Chilean Turco in the following manner: "With its tail erect, and stiltlike legs, it may be seen every now and then popping from one bush to another with uncommon quickness."

GRAY GALLITO
Rhinocrypta lanceolata
Argentina, Paraguay   8 in.

OCELLATED TAPACULO
Acropternis orthonyx
Andes, Venezuela
to Ecuador   9 in.

The forest tapaculos are usually solitary, but those that live in open country often travel about in small flocks when they are not nesting. They are notably loud-voiced, with a repertoire of weird, harsh clucks, cackles, and gobbles.

The tapaculos' nesting habits are varied. Some forest species nest in rock crevices or in hollow tree trunks close to the ground. The Gray Gallito builds a bulky domed nest of grasses and bark with a side entrance, usually 2 or 3 feet up in a thick thornbush. The Brown Gallito, which the Argentinians call the "barrancolina," or little bank-dweller, digs a narrow 3-inch tunnel a foot or so into a bank, ending in a rounded chamber which the birds cushion with grass for their two white eggs. The Chilean Turko is also a tunnel nester.

Tapaculos' courtship and incubation have never been described, and little is known of the fledgling stages except that the hatchlings have a sparse down and are reared in the nest by both parents. Birds in their first juvenile plumage show conspicuous rusty bands.

COTINGAS

PASSERIFORMES   COTINGIDAE

This is a large and diverse family of New World primitive passerines. Among 91 species of some 30 genera are some of the gaudiest and most striking of all neotropical birds, as well as many that are drab and nondescript. Cotingas range in size from 3½ to 20 inches. Some are crested; some have brilliant patches of bare skin on the head; some have fleshy wattles or excrescenses about the bill; and one group has a weird feathered lappet hanging from the throat. Despite their great variation in color, size, and form, all cotingas are united by a combination of anatomical characteristics involving the peculiar structure of their vocal organs and of their legs and feet. They are most closely related to the manakins and to the tyrant flycatchers, which several of the smaller cotingas resemble in appearance and habits.

Cotingas are essentially solitary forest dwellers, usually encountered singly or in pairs, occasionally in small family groups with young. They occupy all types of woodland from the heaviest rainforests to the pine and oak cover of the highlands. Most live in the treetops or in the middle stories of the jungle, a few in the brushy forest edges; one small group, the cocks-of-the-rock, is terrestrial.

Cotingas are most common in tropical forests along the Amazon and in southern Central America. From this center representatives of the family have spread southward to Paraguay, Bolivia, and northern Argentina, and northward to the southern border of the United States. A single species, the Jamaican Becard, has secured a foothold in the highlands of Jamaica and is the only member of the family found in the West Indies.

"Cotinga" comes from the Amazon Indians' name for one of the more bizarre members of the family, the White Bellbird, and means literally "washed white." This bird of the deep forest, the Snowy Cotinga, and several other close relatives are among the very few white or mostly white tropical forest birds. White occurs sparingly in land birds, except in those of the snowy arctic regions, and its natural advantage, if any, to these birds of the dark tropical jungles has never been satisfactorily explained.

Many of the cotingas are almost as conspicuous in other bright, gay colors as the few white species. They exhibit lovely and unusual shades of reds, purples, and blues. These colors occur mainly in the males, the females' being drabber browns and grays. Unfortunately we know little of how the males use them in display, for most cotingas carry out their courtship in the privacy of the high leafy treetops.

The cotingas' unusual colors, particularly the violet shades, are not produced by a prismatic feather structure that refracts light, as are most such colors in birds, but by a true pigment within the feathers. This pigment has been isolated and is known as cotingin. An example of it is the lovely red lavender of the Pompadour Cotinga, which was named not for any peculiarity of its own but for the noted French courtesan who made the upswept hairdo famous. Madame de Pompadour set a fashion of elaborate coiffures adorned with ribbons, flowers, feathers, and even whole birds.

The first specimen of this unusual bird to reach Europe was in a shipment of bright-colored bird skins sent to Madame de Pompadour for this purpose from French Guiana. The French ship carrying it from Cayenne was captured by the British, and George Edwards, the eccentric British naturalist and artist who first described and portrayed the bird, gallantly named it in honor of its intended recipient.

Edwards, and other 18th-century European naturalists who knew nothing of cotingas' habits and behavior, called them

MASKED TITYRA ♂
Tityra semifasciata
Mexico to Brazil and Bolivia   8 in.

BLACK-NECKED RED COTINGA ♂
Phoenicircus nigricollis
Northern Brazil   9 in.

"chatterers" from their fancied resemblance to waxwings. No name could be more unfitting. No cotinga can possibly be said to chatter and many are notably quiet. Some have faintly musical lisping subsongs; some make grunting, rumbling, unbirdlike sounds; a few utter shrill whistles. The notes of the bellbirds are loud, explosive metallic peals that carry half a mile or more through the jungle.

The four bellbirds are odd-looking, jay-sized fruit-eaters. The White Bellbird has a peculiar erectile black spike sparsely covered with small white feathers growing from the base of its upper bill. The male Naked-throated Bellbird of south-

THREE-WATTLED BELLBIRD ♂
Procnias tricarunculata
Nicaragua to Panama   11½ in.

LOVELY COTINGA ♂
Cotinga amabilis
Mexico to Costa Rica   7½ in.

eastern Brazil is also pure white, but instead of the wattle has a verdigris throat and face, bare of feathers but covered with scattered bristles. The male Black-winged Bellbird of Trinidad, Venezuela, and the Guianas has thin fleshy wattles hanging from its throat. This bird's body is white, with the wings black and the head brown. The females of both these species are soft-olive-green birds with blended yellow markings. The Three-wattled Bellbird of Middle America has, as shown in the illustration on page 29, three pronounced wattles, and it displays with its mouth wide open.

Several cotingas show peculiar aberrant development of the wing feathers. One such is the curled coverts of the Pompadour Cotinga. Others have one or two of the outer primaries twisted or sharply narrowed. Whether these abnormalities are used for courtship display is uncertain.

Most singular of these anomalies in the cotingas are those of the crowlike umbrellabirds, so named for their crests of retractile feathers which they expand like a parasol when displaying. Each of these birds also has an inflatable lappet hanging from its throat. In the 20-inch ornate Umbrellabird shown on page 31, the lappet is feathered and sometimes reaches 13 inches in length. In other subspecies the lappet is shorter, and in one it is unfeathered and bright red. Little is known about how the umbrellabirds use these excrescences, for they are birds of the treetops and have been little studied. Like the bellbirds, they are fruit eaters.

Another group of treetop-inhabiting, fruit-eating cotingas is the fruit-crows. The Crimson Fruit-crow, an 18-inch strawberry-colored bird found in eastern Brazil and the Guianas, is one of the larger members of the family. The smaller 11-inch Purple-throated Fruit-crow ranges from Costa Rica southward through the Amazon region. Black with a patch of stiff, glossy maroon feathers on its throat, at a distance it resembles a stout, heavy-bodied jay.

Among the handsomest of the family are the two cocks-of-the-rock, the males of which are a bright orange in one species, a soft red in the other, while the females are a warm

1 UMBRELLABIRD ♂
Cephalopterus ornatus
Costa Rica to Brazil   20 in.

2 GUIANAN COCK-OF-THE-ROCK ♂
Rupicola rupicola
Guianas and
northern Brazil   12 in.

3 ANDEAN COCK-OF-THE-ROCK ♂
Rupicola peruviana
Northern Andes, Colombia to Peru   12 in.

4 POMPADOUR COTINGA ♂
Xipholena punicea
Guianas and
northeastern Brazil   8 in.

brown. Their outstanding feature is the large, flattened, disk-like crest extending from the top of the head to the tip of the bill. Terrestrial birds of the undergrowth and forest floor, the cocks-of-the-rock have stronger, heavier feet than other cotingas, and have a communal courtship dance reminiscent of the Sage Grouse's. Groups of up to a score of males and females gather in a forest clearing, and one male at a time goes through a series of hopping antics to show off before the females. Cock-of-the-rock nests are shallow mud cups reinforced with sticks and decorated with leaves. The few that have been found were on ledges near the mouths of sheltered caves near jungle streams.

A better-known group of cotingas is made up of the three tityras, the commonest being the Masked Tityra which occurs from Mexico to Brazil, not only in the rainforests but in drier areas with scattered trees. Though birds of the treetops, the tityras are frequently found in the open where they are easily observed. Small flocks or family parties rove through the woodlands in search of the fruits and berries that compose the greater part of their diet. They also eat quantities of insects, which they occasionally catch in flight but more often snatch from the foliage. Tityras are vaguely shrikelike in appearance, with sharply hooked bills, but they are chunkier, heavier-bodied, and have shorter necks and larger heads. In the bright tropical sunlight the light gray of the male tityras looks almost white, contrasting with the black marks on the wings and tail. The brown-backed female Masked Tityra lacks the male's black forehead, and her bare facial patches are not so red. Their voices are strange froglike croakings.

Tityras nest in high tree cavities, which they usually appropriate from other species. They drive away the owners, usually woodpeckers or toucans, by filling the hole with twigs and leaves in their absence. This they keep up until the rightful proprietors tire of cleaning away the mess and abandon the site. The only tityra nest ever examined (they are hard to reach, high up in precarious dead stubs) contained two buffy brown eggs heavily marbled with darker brown, almost buried in the leaf litter lining the cavity. Incubation is by the female alone. The male stands by to guard the hole during her frequent absences on feeding trips, and helps feed the young. The incubation period has never been determined, but the young remain in the nest 3 weeks or more. Tityras are multibrooded, and often lay a second clutch of eggs a few weeks after the first young leave the nest.

The 15 species of becards are found through most of the family's range. Becards are small dull-colored birds 5 to 8 inches long with large heads and thick, slightly hooked beaks (hence their name). Blacks, grays, and brown predominate in their coloring, with the females always less imposing than their mates. The northernmost species, the Rose-throated Becard, nests from the Arizona and Texas border southward to Costa Rica.

Like most cotingas, the becards live mostly in the treetops, but occasionally forage at lower levels. They eat some berries and small fruits, but their diet is chiefly insects, which they capture both in flight and from the foliage. A favorite method of feeding is by hovering close to the leaves of outer branches and plucking caterpillars without alighting.

Becards build large, bulky nests of twigs and leaves, domed over the top, with the entrance at the side or through the bottom. They make no attempt to conceal these imposing structures, but usually build them in plain sight near the end of a branch at some height above the ground. They often build near nests of stinging wasps, a habit adopted by many tropical species, apparently for protection.

The female becard does most, if not all, the nest building. In some species the male brings nesting material. The clutch varies from 3 to 6 eggs, which are usually buff-colored, variously marked with brown. Incubation, so far as known, is entirely by the female, and takes 18 to 19 days in one of the smaller species, the 5½-inch White-winged Becard of Panama, one of the very few cotingas whose incubation period is known. The young are fed by both parents, almost entirely on insects, and remain in the nest 3 weeks or longer.

PEARL-HEADED MANAKIN
Pipra iris
Northern Brazil 3½ in.

WIRE-TAILED MANAKIN ♂
Teleonema filicauda
Venezuela and Colombia to Peru 5 in.

RED-CAPPED (YELLOW-THIGHED) MANAKIN
Pipra mentalis
Mexico to Ecuador 4½ in.

MANAKINS

PASSERIFORMES   PIPRIDAE

The pert, bright-eyed, active, chubby manakins are among
the most conspicuous small birds of American tropical and
subtropical forests. The bright colors of the males, their constant activity, comparative tameness, and unusual songs make
them more noticeable than many species just as common and
several times their size. Residents of woodlands from southern
Mexico to Paraguay and northern Argentina, their center of
abundance is Venezuela, the Guianas, and Brazil.

Unlike their nearest relatives, the cotingas, the 59 species
of manakins form a fairly homogenous group. All are tiny
birds, most less than 5 inches long. The few that exceed 6
inches are no larger in body size, but have longer tails that

add a few inches to their length. Typically their tails and wings are short, their legs and feet are slender, and their middle front toe is joined at the base to one or the other of its neighbors. The manakins' stubby beaks are broad at the base and pointed at the tip. The upper mandible overhangs the lower slightly, and has a small notch near the end.

In most manakins the sexes differ. The males have brilliant patches of red, yellow, or blue on the head, back, or thighs that contrast vividly with their brownish-green to velvety-black bodies. The females are all little olive-green birds that are likely to escape notice as they flit quietly through the forest. In one small relatively unstudied group, which may be misplaced in this family, the sexes are alike. This group includes the Thrushlike Manakin (*Schiffornis*), a rather shy and secretive reddish-brown bird that lives in forest undergrowth from Mexico to Brazil.

Manakins wander through the forest singly or in small bands. They feed on small berries and insects, and a few can usually be found in the mixed flocks of antbirds, tanagers, and other insect eaters that follow army-ant trains for the small animal life they panic out of hiding. Manakins seldom pick insects from the ground, but snatch those that climb into the foliage to escape the ants. They swallow small insects at once; larger ones they pound to pieces with their bills. Manakins show little fear of man, and go about their business near him as unconcerned as titmice.

The noises the manakins make include strange unbirdlike sounds—sharp crackings like the snapping of a dry stick or a flag whipping in the wind, and odd mechanical raspings as though a nail were drawn across a comb. The call notes their primitive vocal organs produce are simple unobtrusive chirps and thin, high-pitched whistles. A few sing melodious, bell-like little songs of low intensity and short duration. Their spectacular noises are made mechanically with their wings. The flight feathers of most male manakins show peculiar modifications, apparently for this purpose. In the Yellow-thighed Manakin, the secondary wing feathers are enlarged, stiffened, and curved. In some species the outer primaries are narrowed at the tip; in a few they are twisted. The long-tailed species usually have the bases of the primaries curiously thickened. Just how the rattlings and buzzings are produced has yet to be demonstrated conclusively—whether by the wings striking each other, by the shafts vibrating together, or by air rushing between the feathers. When producing these sounds, the birds flutter their wings too rapidly for the eye to follow.

In several manakins whose breeding habits have been well studied the males are highly polygamous, and this pattern is apparently the rule in all the sexually dimorphic species. At the start of the breeding season (in January or February north of the equator), the males repair to a suitable part of the forest and establish individual display territories where they go through a highly intricate series of antics, calling attention to themselves by dancing about, flashing their bright colors, and making their loud noises. These dancing grounds may be isolated, but in some species a score or more males may have territories within the space of a few acres.

Gould's and Black-and-white manakins each establish display territories between two small saplings a few feet apart. Each bird cleans the jungle floor between them bare of all leaves and litter. At intervals the males flit back and forth between their two saplings, springing from one to the other and back again, buzzing and snapping with their wings at each flit. Male Yellow-thighed Manakins set up dancing territories higher in trees. Each picks a bare branch in an open spot in the foliage from which to execute its bouncing, snapping displays.

When a female approaches, the males increase their activity; each makes short buzzing flights to show his charms. When the female makes her choice there is no poaching, and no nearby males leave their territories. After copulating the female flies away as quietly as she came. The males remain on their territories throughout the breeding season, and each presumably serves as many females as he attracts.

Each female builds her nest, incubates her eggs, and rears her young by herself. She may build near the male's territory, or some distance from it. She weaves a frail little basket of grass and fibers between the forks of a horizontal branch from 5 to 75 feet above the ground, depending on the species. She lays two spotted eggs which she incubates for 19 to 21 days. She feeds the young by regurgitating insects and occasional berries carried to the nest in her throat. The young fledge in about 2 weeks.

In their juvenile plumage, the young males resemble adult females. They retain this plumage most of their first year, and some come into breeding condition while still wearing it. This may account for the occasional reports in the literature of females taking an active part in the courtship dances.

TYRANT FLYCATCHERS

PASSERIFORMES   TYRANNIDAE

This large New World family of insect-eaters is the most aggressive and the most successful, biologically speaking, of the primitive passerine groups. Its 367 species are widely spread over the Americas from the tree limit across northern Canada southward to Patagonia. The Tyrannidae are most plentiful in tropical lowlands, where they probably originated, but they have spread into the temperate zones to occupy successfully almost every available ecological niche where insects are to be found. Almost all tyrant flycatchers are arboreal, except for a few terrestrial species in southern South America that hunt insects on the ground somewhat like pipits. These aberrant flycatchers have longer, stronger legs than the rest of the family, and are more gregarious.

Like all primitive passerines, tyrant flycatchers have a comparatively simple voice box. The partial joining of two of their front toes at the base and other similarities show their relationship to the cotingas and the manakins, with which they doubtless shared a common ancestor millions of years ago— in earliest Tertiary time if not earlier. Their superficial resemblances to many species of the large family of Old World flycatchers in appearance and habits are the result of convergent evolution. The Old World family consists of oscines that apparently arose at a later date from an unrelated parent stock on the other side of the world.

Most of the tyrants are plain-colored birds, mainly olive-green, brown, and gray. The sexes are usually alike; only in a few bright-colored species do the females differ markedly from the males. Despite their somber garbs, the tyrants are conspicuous, for they are active, audacious, and often quite noisy. They like to forage in the open, where they are easy to see. Some of the smaller species are so alike that it is next to impossible to tell them apart in the field, but most are easy to recognize as members of the tyrant flycatcher family. Their peculiar upright perching stance is unmistakable.

Tyrant flycatchers range in size from 3½ to 16 inches, but typically they are medium to small birds less than 10 inches in length, with large heads and flattish beaks, which are strongly hooked in all the northern species, less so in some tropical forms. Most have prominent bristles at the base of the bills. Their wings are usually pointed, their tails rounded to shallowly forked—deeply forked in a few long-tailed species. Their legs and feet are small and weak.

In most of the family the crown feathers are more or less erectile. Many species have a distinct crest, often with a streak of bright red, yellow, or white feathers in the center that may or may not be partly concealed. The birds use the crest both for display and intimidation, raising and expanding it to show the color mostly in moments of stress. The crest reaches its greatest development in the little Royal Flycatcher, a resident of rainforests from Mexico through Brazil. Despite

1 VERMILION FLYCATCHER ♂
Pyrocephalus rubinus
Southwestern U.S. to Argentina   5½ in.

2 SCISSOR-TAILED FLYCATCHER
Muscivora forficata
South-central United States   15 in.

3 EASTERN KINGBIRD
Tyrannus tyrannus
Central and eastern North America   9 in.

**4 GREAT CRESTED
FLYCATCHER**
Myiarchus crinitus
Eastern North America   9 in.

5 EASTERN PHOEBE
Sayornis phoebe
Eastern North America   7 in.

its flaming crown, the Royal Flycatcher is not conspicuous in the half-light of the lower and middle stories of its tropical forest home. It keeps its crest lowered and its colors hidden except when excited.

Most flycatchers feed in a distinctive manner by capturing insects on the wing in short sallies from a prominent perch, where they sit quietly upright and alert until their quarry ventures within range. Then they dash out suddenly, snap their prey out of the air with an audible click of the bill, and return with it to their perch to eat at leisure. They often beat large insects loudly against the perch to get bite-size pieces for swallowing. Insects are their mainstay, and they consume practically any and all kinds. Some of the smaller species hunt through trees like vireos or warblers, scouring the foliage for their prey. A number of flycatchers supplement their diet with small berries. These genera usually have the rictal bristles poorly developed. The larger species, like the strong-beaked Boat-billed Flycatcher, pick up small reptiles and amphibians when they can, and the Derby Flycatcher has learned to catch fish.

Among the more conspicuous of the North American members of the family are the kingbirds of the nominate genus *Tyrannus*. Kingbirds are aptly named, for they are indeed monarchs who brook no intrusion into their nesting territories by birds many times their size. Typical of the group is the familiar Eastern Kingbird, a common roadside bird east of the Mississippi which the Indians, who knew it well before the white man came, called "Little Chief." This 9-inch bundle of feathered ferocity is unmistakable with its dark back, white breast, and white-tipped tail. Concealed within its crest is a crown of orange which it flashes when courting or when angry. From its commanding perch on a fencepost, bush, or telephone wire, the Kingbird dashes out fearlessly to harass every passing crow, hawk, or other large bird that dares trespass on its domain. Invariably the trespasser flees ignominiously, but the Kingbird keeps attacking until the interloper is well on his way. The Kingbird's fearlessness and audacity have made it a favorite with all who know birds—all except apiarists, who resentfully call it the "bee martin." Bee stings hold no terrors for the Kingbirds, and their inroads on hives of honeybees can be considerable.

Other North American flycatchers are less showy than the Kingbird in appearance as well as actions, and many lack conspicuous field marks. A number so closely resemble one another, particularly the little olive-green members of the genus *Empidonax,* that they are the despair of bird watchers. Three of these "empidonaces," the Least, the Acadian, and the Alder (or Traill's) flycatchers, can be told apart only with difficulty even from specimens in the hand. They are most easily recognized in the field by their distinctive calls, but this is little help when they are migrating in the fall, for the birds are then quite silent. Skilled field observers often have to list migrants they see as *"Empidonax,* sp.?," meaning they are certain of the genus only, not the species.

Many of the flycatchers are exceedingly vocal, and their voices are so distinctive that a number have named themselves. The dull-colored little Wood Pewee of our northern forests utters his plaintive "pee-a-wee" all day long until it actually gets tiresome. Another flycatcher that announces itself is the Phoebe, the pert olive-gray bird that plasters its mud and moss nest under bridges over country streams. The Pewee and the Phoebe usually call incessantly from a perch; the Kingbird utters its harsh grating chatter in flight.

In common with most insect-eaters that nest in temperate latitudes, all the North American flycatchers migrate southward when winter cuts down the food on which they depend. Phoebes winter in the Southern states and never go south of Mexico, but other northern flycatchers travel on to Central America and northern South America. Most are night migrants, but the Kingbirds travel by day in loose, widely scattered waves. A few of the flycatchers that breed in the high mountains of Central and South America migrate vertically, moving up and down the slopes with the seasons.

One of the few tyrants that migrates in flocks is the lovely

GREAT KISKADEE (DERBY FLYCATCHER)
Pitangus sulphuratus
South Texas to Argentina   9 in.

ACADIAN FLYCATCHER
Empidonax virescens
Eastern United States   6 in.

EASTERN WOOD PEWEE
Contopus virens
Eastern North America   6½ in.

**NORTHERN ♂
ROYAL FLYCATCHER**
Onychorhynchus mexicanus
Mexico to Venezuela   6½ in.

Scissor-tailed Flycatcher, whose long, trailing, deeply forked tail makes it the longest (16 inches) of the family, though shorter species surpass it in body size. The Scissor-tail breeds in the open lands of the south-central United States and is a conspicuous inhabitant of the Texas plains, where it sits quietly on telephone wires and trees along the roadsides, a trim symphony in pastel pink and gray, with its long tail closed and hanging straight down. Its flight in pursuit of prey or when chasing an intruder from its guarded preserve is dashing and swift with rapidly fluttering wings, tail streaming straight behind. The Scissor-tail is also fond of performing acrobatics high in the air, flying in erratic zigzags with abrupt sharp turns facilitated by pivoting on its widely spread tail. It winters from Mexico to Panama, traveling by daylight and often in sizable flocks.

The most brightly colored member of the family is the fiery male Vermilion Flycatcher, resident from southwestern United States southward through Central and South America to Argentina. Strangely, this brilliant little bird has never reached the West Indies, but is well established on most of the Galapagos Islands 500 miles out in the Pacific west of Ecuador. It is one of the few flycatchers that show strong sexual dimorphism, the female being a dull brownish gray.

Among the many distinctive tropical species, one of the most familiar is the large, stout-bodied, brown and yellow Derby Flycatcher, widely known as the Kiskadee from its rasping cry, paraphrased as "kiss-me-dear" by the romantic, as "qu'est ce qu'il dit?" by the French, as *bem-te-vi* (I see thee well) by the Brazilian Portuguese, and as *bien-te-veo* by Spanish-speaking peoples. The Kiskadee is a noisy, conspicuous busybody found from southern Texas to Argentina in semi-open lands, and is common almost wherever there are trees. Though essentially insectivorous, the Kiskadee also frequents mangroves and other riverside vegetation in the tidelands, where it has acquired an un-flycatcherlike habit—it fishes like a kingfisher, splashing boldly into the water for small fish.

The nesting habits of flycatchers are considerably varied.

Typically they weave open, cup-shaped nests of grasses and twigs in trees. The Phoebe builds a mud base for its nest of moss under a streamside ledge or under bridge rafters. Many tropical species make large purse-shaped or domed nests with an entrance at the side or in the bottom. Some of the Brazilian and Argentinian species appropriate the mud-and-stick nests built by ovenbirds. Not a few species are cavity nesters, like the Great Crested Flycatcher of eastern North America which stuffs its untidy nest into old woodpecker holes, bird boxes, open-ended mail boxes, or even into the metal receptacles put up for the daily paper along rural roads.

The Crested Flycatcher's fondness for decorating its nest with cast-off snakeskins has provoked much speculation. The oft-proposed theory that the birds use pieces of snakeskin consciously as a protective measure to frighten predators is hardly tenable. Its use is probably fortuitous, as a convenient material of desirable consistency. Pieces of cellophane and waxed paper occur just as frequently in the nests. Unquestionably protective, however, is the common flycatcher habit of building their nests near those of wasps.

The eggs of different species of flycatchers also show considerable variation. Some are pure white; others are spotted or streaked. Clutches vary from 2 to 6 and are usually smaller in tropical species, many of which maintain their numbers by nesting several times instead of once per year as do most temperate zone species, though these also are sometimes multibrooded.

While both sexes cooperate in nest building, the usual pattern in flycatchers is for the female alone to incubate. Rarely does the male assist in this duty, though he always helps feed the nestlings. The incubation period varies from 12 days in the species building open nests to as many as 21 days in some of those that build covered hanging nests where the clutch is accessible to predation. The young flycatchers remain in the nest for a roughly equal length of time before taking flight.

PLANTCUTTERS

PASSERIFORMES   PHYTOTOMIDAE

In temperate South America, from western Peru southward to Patagonia, live three species of chunky, finchlike birds that look so much like grosbeaks they were for many years thought to be sparrows. Their syrinx muscles and their foot structure, however, show them to be related to the cotingas, from which they differ mainly in the arrangement of their thigh muscles and in their finchlike conical bills, which are short, strong, and finely sawtoothed.

Each of the three plantcutters is about 7 inches in length. The sexes differ in color. Best known and most widespread is the Reddish Plantcutter of Argentina, Uruguay, and Bolivia. The female is brownish and sparrowlike. The Peruvian Plantcutter, isolated along the dry northwest coast of Peru, has less red in its plumage; the Chilean species is gray.

Plantcutters live in open woodlands, dry brushy country, and in cultivated regions. They earn their name by their gross manner of feeding; they clip off leaves, buds, fruits, and shoots, and sever small plants at the base, wasting far more than they eat. In farming country, particularly in Chile, they are reported occasionally so destructive to crops and gardens that control measures are necessary. Plantcutters are often rather tame and fearless, and permit a close approach as they perch quiet and upright on top of a bush. When disturbed they seldom fly far, but take cover in nearby foliage. Their flight is weak and undulating and seldom prolonged. They flutter their short, pointed wings rapidly enough in flight to produce an audible whirring.

Plantcutters often gather in small, loose flocks that move erratically about the countryside when the breeding season is over, and show some seasonal movement in shifting their feeding grounds. Their harsh and unmusical calls have been likened to the squeaking of tree limbs rubbing together, to the croaking of frogs, and to the bleatings of lambs.

Plantcutters build open round nests of twigs lined with finer vegetable fibers. The Chilean Plantcutter nests fairly high in trees; the Reddish Plantcutter usually nests closer to the ground, often in the sanctuary of a thorn bush. The clutch is 2 to 4 bluish-green eggs spotted with dark brown. Incubation is by the female alone; care of the young is by both sexes.

SHARPBILLS

PASSERIFORMES   OXYRUNCIDAE

Little is known about the sharpbills beyond what the few scattered museum specimens reveal. They have been collected in six countries: Costa Rica, Panama, Venezuela, British Guiana, southeastern Brazil, and Paraguay. Nowhere are they plentiful, and each known population seems to be extremely localized. The Brazilian and Paraguayan groups live in lowland rainforests 3,000 feet or so above sea level. Specimens from the six widely scattered localities differ slightly in size (6½ to 7 inches) and in the yellow to white shading of their underparts. All are regarded as geographical representatives of a single species which was probably more widespread and of continuous distribution in the distant past.

The sharpbills have no close relatives and their systematic position is uncertain. Anatomically they seem closest to the tyrant flycatchers, for they have the same type of syrinx muscles and foot structure. The partly concealed bright-red median crest (usually paler in females) is strongly reminiscent of that of many of the tyrants, but sharpbills' legs and toes are stouter and stronger. They differ markedly from the tyrants in their straight, sharp-pointed, unhooked bills, which are uniquely rimmed at the base with short, fine, bristly feathers instead of with rictal bristles. Their nostrils are covered by an opercular flap, and are elongated instead of round. Pending further research that may show their affinities more clearly, most students place them in a family by themselves.

No one has observed sharpbills enough in life to describe their habits and behavior. They are apparently solitary birds; at least, flocks have never been reported. They are known to eat fruit. Their actions in the field reminded one collector of those of the Old World wrynecks; others who have seen them report that they act like cotingas or tanagers. Their breeding habits are unknown and their nests and eggs have never been described.

CRESTED SHARPBILL ♂
Oxyruncus cristatus
Costa Rica to Paraguay   7 in.

REDDISH PLANTCUTTER ♂
Phytotoma rutila
Bolivia, Paraguay,
Uruguay, Argentina   7 in.

GARNET PITTA
Pitta granatina
Malaya, Sumatra,
Borneo 6½ in.

STEERE'S PITTA
Pitta steerii
Philippines 8 in.

PITTAS

PASSERIFORMES   PITTIDAE

Plump-bodied small birds from 6 to 11 inches in length, pittas have stout, slightly down-curved bills, large heads, short necks, short rounded wings, and rather long, strong legs and feet. Their most distinctive feature, other than the variegated gay coloring of their loose-webbed plumage, is their abnormally short, stumpy tails. These have degenerated in some species to mere tufts of short, stiff feathers. A few species have a crest or ear tufts. In each species the sexes are similarly colored in a gaudy assortment of contrasting patches that includes almost the entire spectrum from greens to purples, reds, and yellows. The females are usually duller than the males.

Technically the pittas are a distinctive and closely knit group, so close that all 23 recognized species are placed in the single genus *Pitta*. Their center of distribution is southeastern Asia and adjacent Malaysia. A single species, the Blue-winged, or Fairy, Pitta, ranges from northern India across China to southern Japan. Others are found eastward to the Philippines and to the Solomons and southward to Australia, where three species occur. Two species are isolated in eastern and central Africa. Many of the tropical pittas are of extremely limited distribution. One of the most beautiful, Steere's Pitta, lives only in the mossy undergrowth of the wet mountain forests of three of the Philippine Islands.

The pittas have no close relatives, and their affinities to other existing families are uncertain. Their primitive syrinx structure is responsible for their placement in the suborder Tyranni, to whose New World members they show no other close ties. Their homogeneity as a group and their disrupted distribution suggest the living pittas are the surviving representatives of a primitive stock of forest-inhabiting birds formerly more widely distributed over the Old World tropics.

The pittas' bright hues are seldom seen to best advantage in the dim light of their usual habitat, the floor and lower stories of wet, tropical forests. These solitary birds stay in the thickest cover, where they are hard to see. When approached they scurry away through the underbrush like some rodent. When pittas do fly, they fly straight and fast with rapid wingbeats. Many are migratory. Those that nest in temperate China, Japan, and Australia winter in the tropics, and several of the tropical forms are believed to move to fresh feeding grounds in the nonbreeding season.

Pittas feed entirely on insects and other small animal life. Some species live largely on termites, others on millepedes. The Noisy Pitta, whose showy colors have earned it the name of "dragoon bird" in Australia, is fond of slugs and land snails, and usually has a particular stump or stone within its territory that it uses for cracking open their shells.

Though the pittas feed and spend most of their days on

the ground, they roost in trees at night, and usually hop up into the branches when calling. Their call notes are loud double- or triple-noted whistles of considerable carrying power, but so ventriloquial they are difficult to trace to their source. Some pittas call to one another across the jungle on moonlight nights; others make peculiar grunting noises. The African species make whirring and rattling sounds, apparently with their wings, in short courtship flights.

Pittas build large globular nests, loosely put together of twigs and vegetable fibers, with an entrance on the side. The nest is usually on or near the ground, often in a thorny bush, but may be as high as 30 feet up a tree.

Pitta eggs are almost round, highly glossed, white to buffy in color, and covered with flecks of dark brown. The normal clutch is 4 to 6, though as few as 2 and as many as 7 eggs have been reported. Both parents incubate and care for the altricial young, but the length of the incubation period has not been determined accurately. The northern species breed from May to August; those south of the equator in Africa and Australia breed in the southern summer, from November to February. The oriental tropical species tend to nest during the rainy season from February to April, probably because their insect food is then most plentiful.

NEW ZEALAND WRENS

PASSERIFORMES   ACANTHISITTIDAE

Four species of tiny, insect-eating New Zealand birds constitute this family. Three are 4-inch brownish, wrenlike birds (*Xenicus*) that scurry with their tails cocked up through the underbrush or on rocky ground. The fourth (*Acanthisitta*) is the 3-inch, yellowish-green Rifleman, New Zealand's smallest bird, a creeperlike inhabitant of deep forests.

The Rifleman is still fairly common, though limited to the beech forests. The Bush Wren and Rock Wren are now rare, having suffered from such introduced predators as stoats, rats, and cats. The Stephen Island Wren is extinct. It had probably the most limited range of any known bird—a wooded islet scarcely a mile in area in Cook Strait.

The extant species are weak fliers. The most capable of the three, the Rock Wren, is able to flutter only a hundred feet or so. Their primitive vocal organs produce simple nasal chirps, calls, and alarm notes, but no true song. All three build covered nests with side entrances, the Rifleman in tree cavities, the two wrens in hollow logs or stumps, rock crevices, or holes in the ground. Their clutches range from 2 to 5 pure-white eggs, and both sexes share the nesting chores.

The affinities of these distinctive tiny birds are uncertain, but they show similarities in structure and behavior to the pittas. They probably evolved from some remote pittalike ancestor that became isolated in New Zealand long ago.

BUSH WREN
Xenicus longipes
New Zealand 3½ in.

ASITIES AND
FALSE SUNBIRDS

PASSERIFORMES   PHILEPITTIDAE

In the forests of Madagascar live four little-known small birds that are evidently the sole survivors of some primitive passerine stock that has long since vanished elsewhere in the world. Though quite different in build and habits, the two asities (*Philepitta*) and two false sunbirds (*Neodrepanis*) share anatomical characteristics that suggest they evolved from the same ancestor.

The asities are plump, stout-legged, completely arboreal birds that vaguely resemble pittas. The commoner Velvet Asity inhabits the humid forests on the eastern slopes from sea level to 5,000 feet. It is reported as a quiet, stolid bird, that allows a close approach. It works rather sluggishly through the middle stories and brushy ground cover of the forest in search of fruits and berries, usually alone, sometimes in small parties of two or three. Its voice is seldom heard, but it has a soft, thrushlike song. The only member of the family whose nesting is known, the Velvet Asity weaves a hanging, pear-shaped nest of mosses and palm fibers, lined with dead leaves. The side entrance is sheltered by a small portico. The one clutch reported contained three white eggs. On the western side of Madagascar lives Schlegel's Asity, a smaller and more brightly colored bird.

Sharing the wet forests of the eastern slopes with the Velvet Asity is the Wattled False Sunbird, a much smaller and very different species, with small, weak legs and a long curved bill. So closely does it resemble the true sunbirds that for years it was classified as one until anatomical studies showed its true affinities. It lives and feeds exactly as do the sunbirds, dipping into flowers to sip nectar and pick up small insects. Like the asities, it is a solitary bird, and, though reportedly not uncommon, seldom are more than two or three seen together. Its call is a soft hissing note. The second false sunbird, the Small-billed Neodrepanis, is known from seven specimens taken in the forests of northeastern Madagascar. It is a small, inconspicuous bird, apparently easily overlooked and, like all the unique Madagascar fauna, in danger of extinction as its forest habitat disappears.

**WATTLED
FALSE SUNBIRD**
Neodrepanis coruscans
Eastern Madagascar   3½ in.

VELVET ASITY
Philepitta castanea
Eastern Madagascar   6½ in.

LYREBIRDS

PASSERIFORMES   MENURIDAE

Not the least of the marvels of Australia, that continent of many zoological and botanical anomalies, are the wonderful lyrebirds, so named from the tail of the male Superb Lyrebird, which in certain positions resembles the instrument that Orpheus smote. Two species constitute the family, the Superb and the slightly smaller Albert's Lyrebird, named for Prince Albert, Queen Victoria's consort. Brown-backed, ashy-bellied birds the size of a rooster with elongated pointed bills, longish necks, large, strong legs and feet, and fantastic long tails, the first lyrebirds to reach Europe at the close of the 18th century were thought to be pheasants by the naturalists who studied them.

Much later, when their anatomy was studied, the lyrebirds were found to have an oscine type of syrinx, but with only 3 pairs of muscles instead of the oscine's 5 to 7. Other anatomical peculiarities include their long, narrow breastbone, which resembles that of most water birds rather than the short, squarish passerine type, a tail of 16 feathers instead of the usual 12, and 6 feathers on the thumb joint, or alula, instead of the usual 3 or 4. To show their anomalous systematic position, the lyrebirds are placed with the order Passeriformes, but in a suborder of their own, the Menurae, together with the distantly related Australian scrub-birds.

The Superb Lyrebird is widely familiar through its symbolic use on Australian seals and stamps, where it appears as often as the Emu, the kangaroo, the platypus, and the koala bear. The traditional posture of the bird as pictured on postage stamps and in books, with the tail erect and partly spread into a perfect lyre, has caused Australian ornithologists some embarrassment because it is not typical, though it occurs momentarily during the courtship display.

The frame of the lyre is formed by the outer pair of the male Superb's tail feathers, which are almost 2 feet long and gracefully curved and banded. The next six pairs of quills form the strings; these are brown above and almost white below and, lacking barbules to hold the vanes together, are lacy in texture. The central pair of feathers are long and narrow and lack the outside web; they cross one another just behind their insertion and sweep out gracefully to opposite tips of the lyre. The male Albert's Lyrebird is a redder brown and its fanciful tail lacks the lyre frame. Its central tail feathers are like the Superb's, but all the other seven pairs are lacy quills. The females of both species are colored similarly to the males, but have ordinary tails. Young males resemble the females, and do not develop their distinctive tail plumes until they are about 3 years old.

Both species are residents of the forests and scrublands of eastern Australia, Albert's being the more northerly of the two. They are shy, solitary birds that reportedly keep to thick cover. Largely terrestrial, they seldom fly, but run and leap with great speed through the underbrush. When they do fly they usually glide for considerable distances. At night they roost in the branches of tall trees. Their food is reported as almost entirely animal—insects, worms, land crustaceans, and mollusks which they obtain by scratching like fowl among the leaf litter and by tearing rotten logs apart.

Most famous of the lyrebirds' attributes is their extraordinary skill as mimics. They are credited as being the most accomplished of all birds in this respect, and connoisseurs regard Albert's as the better imitator. While they have distinctive notes of their own, such as the Superb's resounding "choo! choo! choo!" usually heard at dawn, they can reproduce practically all other sounds they hear with fantastic accuracy, especially the calls and songs of other birds. A performing male may give perfect reproductions of the notes of 20 or more species in succession, including the raucous cries of the Kookaburra and the hooting of owls and nightjars. Lyrebirds also copy the cries of animals and mechanical noises—the neighing of a horse, the bleating of sheep, the barking of dogs, the whine of a saw, the sounds of auto horns and motors—in fact anything they hear that strikes their fancy.

Male lyrebirds are thought to be polygynous, for they take no part in nest-building, incubation, or rearing of the young. Each male establishes a large territory for himself, sometimes half a mile or so in extent, within which he tolerates no other males. Within this area he establishes a series of perhaps a dozen display grounds, which he visits in turn throughout the day to perform his magnificent courtship antics. The Superb Lyrebird rakes damp soil into mounds about 3 feet across on which he dances; Albert's Lyrebird scrapes out shallow craters about 2½ feet in diameter.

Climbing his mound or entering his scrape, the displaying male starts his performance vocally, and he chortles and bub-

bles and sings from his extensive repertoire throughout the action. After a few moments of singing he unlimbers his tail, slowly expands it, and raises it up and forward over his back until its shimmering silvery cascade covers him completely, the lacy feather tips touching the ground in front of his lowered head. This is the climax of the display. He ends it suddenly with a few high-pitched notes, folds his tail to its normal position, and stalks away.

The female spends about a month building her nest. On or near the ground, often between two trees, in a hollow stump, or within the crown fronds of a leaning tree fern, she builds a bulky domed structure with a side entrance. Its exterior of sticks, dry fern fronds, moss, and bark has an inner wall

SUPERB LYREBIRD ♂
Menura novaehollandiae
Southeastern Australia   38 in.

woven of rootlets and bark fibers. She lines her nest with long downy feathers she plucks from her back and thighs. A week or so after the nest is finished, she lays her single egg, and she may wait another week before she starts incubating.

The lyrebird egg is dark gray with inky markings, and is the largest laid by any passerine bird. Also the incubation period is the longest reported for any passerine. A lyrebird egg was hatched under a domestic hen in 28 days, but in the wild, lyrebirds are reported to incubate 35 to 40 days. The chick hatches almost naked, but soon grows a covering of long black down. It is raised in the nest in typical passerine fashion, and grows so large before leaving that toward the end of the rearing period it sometimes pokes its head through the domed roof to be fed.

SCRUB-BIRDS

PASSERIFORMES   ATRICHORNITHIDAE

Allied to the lyrebirds and apparently stemming from some common ancestral stock are the two Australian scrub-birds. Little is known of these shy, skulking, brownish birds, somewhat wrenlike in appearance and actions. The larger of the two, the 8½-inch Noisy Scrub-bird, lives in the brushlands of southwestern Australia. Only about 20 museum specimens exist, the last taken in 1889, and it was thought to be extinct until a few were rediscovered in 1961. The slightly smaller Rufous Scrub-bird still persists in small numbers in the subtropical coastal scrublands of eastern Australia. Observers claim it is almost flightless; it flutters feebly for short distances, but can scuttle speedily on ground through the tangled vines and underbrush.

Scrub-birds show affinities to the lyrebirds in having the same oscine type of syrinx, but powered by only two pairs of muscles. Also they have large, strong legs and feet, and scratch the ground for snails, worms, insects, and occasional seeds. Their chief anatomical distinction, probably connected with their weak flight, is their greatly reduced clavicles. They are the only passerine birds in which these two bones are not fused to form a wishbone. The sexes are unlike, the females being duller and smaller.

Scrub-birds further resemble the lyrebirds in vocal powers. They are said to be accomplished mimics, and are famed for their loud and penetrating calls. Those of the male Noisy Scrub-bird were so shrill, one listener reported, "as to produce a ringing sensation in the ears, precisely the effect produced when a shrill whistle is blown in a small room."

The Rufous Scrub-bird builds a miniature version of the lyrebird's domed nest on or close to the ground. Loosely woven of dried grasses and dead leaves, it is lined uniquely with a peculiar tough substance resembling rough cardboard. The birds gather soft decayed wood and plaster it when wet around

RUFOUS SCRUB-BIRD
Atrichornis rufescens
Eastern Australia   7 in.

the inside of the nest. The usual clutch is two pinkish-white eggs speckled with brownish-red. Little is known of their breeding behavior other than that the female alone incubates and rears the young in the nest.

Reduction of habitat and introduced predators are largely responsible for the scrub-birds' rarity. Much of the present range of the Rufous Scrub-bird lies within the boundaries of Lamington National Park, where the bird's chances of survival should be good.

LARKS

PASSERIFORMES   ALAUDIDAE

Small, dull-colored terrestrial birds famed for their inspired song flights, the larks are essentially an Old World group. The family is well represented across Eurasia from the tundra southward, but is best developed in Africa where almost two-thirds of the world's 75 species occur. Two species have pushed southeastward to northern Australia, and a single species, the Horned Lark, has invaded the New World. Readily recognized by its black ear tufts, the Horned Lark breeds circumpolarly in the arctic tundra, southward in the Old World to North Africa, and throughout much of North America to southern Mexico. One isolated population of Horned Larks has established itself in the savannas of the Colombian highlands in South America.

Larks form one of the most distinctive and well-defined of all the passerine families. They differ from all other perching birds in that the back of the tarsus is rounded and scaled instead of sharp and unsegmented. This suggests early differentiation of the family from other passerine stock and, added to certain primitive features of their five-muscled syrinx, places them at or near the base of the oscine family tree—as primitive true singing passerines. The larks' long, pointed wings have 10 primary feathers, but the outermost one is very short, almost obsolete in some genera. The long straight claw on the hind toe, a feature shared with the pipits and wagtails, is another identifying characteristic.

Despite their diversity—the 75 living species are divided among 15 genera—the larks are quite uniform in general appearance, in habitat, and in habits. Small birds, from 5 to 9 inches in length, most of them are somberly clad in streaked browns and grays, darker above than below. All have pointed, slightly down-curved bills and most have crested or tufted heads. Except in the Black Lark of northern Eurasia and the seven finch-larks (*Eremopterix*) of Africa and India, the sexes are similar; the females are sometimes duller and slightly smaller than the males. Some widely distributed larks show minor color or size differences between geographically separated populations. In the widespread Horned Lark, for instance, 15 such subspecies, as these recognizable populations within a species are called, are known in the Old World, 26 in the New.

Most larks live in open country, on grassy plains, treeless moors, cultivated fields, deserts, or beaches. Save for a few species, such as the bush larks that habitually alight on low bushes or posts, they usually dwell on the ground, where they walk or run instead of hopping. They are so well camouflaged that they are not always easy to see until they fly, and usually allow a close approach before they flush. Their diet is almost equally animal and vegetable and encompasses insects and their pupae and larvae, seeds, and other plant material. Larks are generally gregarious, and gather in flocks when not breeding. Most of them are migratory to a degree. Some perform lengthy flights between breeding and wintering grounds.

Larks are renowned as songsters the world over. The spectacular song flight of the courting male Skylark is one of the most beautiful of natural sounds. The Skylark is small, drab, and unpretentious, but his music belies his looks. This is the bird that has inspired so many poets—Shelley, Wordsworth, and Tennyson among them. To know why, you should meet your first one as I did one spring morning in a lonely wheat field. Suddenly a small brown bird whisks from the ground at your feet and spirals swiftly high into the air, showering the countryside with his rippling, bubbling melody.

The "blithe spirit" of Shelley's verse nests across Eurasia from the British Isles to Kamchatka and from northern Siberia southward to India and North Africa. Europeans so love the Skylark they have carried it with them to many other parts of the world. It has been introduced successfully to New Zealand and the Hawaiian Islands. A colony established on Long Island, New York, in the 1880's persisted for a time but gradually died out and has not been reported since 1913. Skylarks introduced to Vancouver Island off British Columbia have fared better and are still thriving.

Despite high sentimental regard for them as songsters, larks were at one time a table delicacy in Europe—witness the lark-

HORNED (SHORE) LARK
Eremophila alpestris
Eurasia, North Africa,
North America, Mexico,
Colombia   6½–7 in.

SKYLARK
Alauda arvensis
Temperate Eurasia,
n. Africa   7 in.

spit of English kitchens. It takes many of the tiny birds to make a meal, but they are still shot and netted for food in parts of the Old World. Such occasional persecution has not seemed to affect their numbers. The forest clearing and field cultivation that accompany human expansion encourage their increase, and larks are quick to expand into new territory where the habitat becomes suitable for them.

Most larks build open, cup-shaped nests on the ground and lay from 2 to 6 speckled white eggs. Exceptions are the bush larks of the genus *Mirafra,* which build domed nests. Incubation is predominantly, if not exclusively, by the female. She builds the nest alone, too, but the male stands by and encourages her with his courtship song flights. He brings her food during the 11 to 12 days she incubates, and helps feed the young for the 10 to 12 days it takes them to fledge. Larks typically rear two or more broods each year.

SWALLOWS AND MARTINS

PASSERIFORMES   HIRUNDINIDAE

No group of birds is more loved by people throughout the world than the swallows and martins. Nearly cosmopolitan in distribution, the family is absent only from the polar regions and a few oceanic islands. "Swallow" goes back to the Old Norse "svalva, and Anglo-Saxon "swalewe." "Martin" is of more recent medieval etymology, but was well established in heraldry. The terms swallow and martin are used somewhat interchangeably today. In America we restrict martin to some of the larger species, but Europeans apply it to a number of the smaller birds we call swallows. The usage seems largely fortuitous, but swallow is more widely used for the family.

Swallows are often confused with the swifts, but are not related to them. Though the two groups resemble each other superficially, they differ widely in anatomy and their similarities are "analogous rather than affinitive," the result of convergent evolution in two discrete stocks that have become adapted to the same ways of living. Though not as thoroughly aerial as swifts, swallows probably spend more of their waking hours on the wing than any other passerine birds.

In the hand swallows can be told at once by their 12-feathered tail (swifts have only 10 rectrices), and by the presence of facial bristles which swifts lack. Swallows have a less speedy and (usually) more erratic flight. Their longer tails are often forked, their bodies less cigar-shaped, and the leading edge of their wings is less smoothly arced.

Otherwise there is no mistaking a swallow or martin. Small birds 4 to 9 inches long, their bodies are slender and sleek, their wings long and pointed. Their plumage is compact, often with some metallic sheen, usually darker above than below. Their legs are short, their feet small and weak. Their tiny triangular bills belie their wide gape, made more effective by bristles which act as an aerial fly scoop.

Though the swallows have their primary feathers reduced from 10 to 9, an indication of high specialization, they are placed low in the passerine family tree because of certain primitive structural features, notably the incomplete development of their bronchial rings. Swallows are indeed highly specialized and peculiarly adapted to an aerial life. They show no close ties with any other avian group. Apparently the family branched off long ago, probably from some primitive perching, insect-eating stock, but just what stock and in what part of the Eocene world is anyone's guess. The 79 living species, in some 20 genera, are scattered so widely and so evenly throughout the world that their distribution affords no clue to their probable place of origin.

Swallows spend much of their time on the wing hawking back and forth for insects. They are exceedingly graceful and among the most accomplished of all fliers, but they are no match for the swifts in speed, and generally do not fly as high. Also unlike the swifts, which alight seldom during the day and then only on vertical surfaces, the swallows perch readily on twigs, branches, wires, and roofs. The only time they are normally seen on the ground is when gathering nesting material. They walk short distances with difficulty and have an awkward shuffling gait.

Swallows are widely beloved because of their value as insect eaters and because they are common, friendly, and attractive birds. While they are not accomplished songsters, they twitter cheerfully and chatter to one another both in flight and at rest. They show little fear of man and nest on and about his dwellings. Not least of the reasons for their popularity in temperate climes both north and south is their ages-old reputation as harbingers of spring.

Few signs of spring are more certain than the appearance of flocks of swallows. As swallows migrate by day and must feed as they travel, their northward advance requires the presence of insects in the air, which in turn depends on warm weather. The swallows' northward migrations coincide nicely with the northward movement of the isotherms that, plotted fortnightly, tell the weatherman spring is on the way. The Barn Swallow usually follows close on the heels of the 48° F. isotherm. One or two hardy individuals often arrive ahead of the main flocks before spring has really settled in and suffer from late freezes, proving the old adage that "one swallow doth not a summer make."

As the swallows' northward movement is governed largely by the weather, it is equally uncertain, and careful records show their arrival dates vary from spring to spring by as much as 2 weeks, which is the normal spread of the isotherm advance. The well-known legend of the swallows that return to the Mission San Juan de Capistrano in California so infallibly on the same day each spring is a charming folk tale, and like many such tales isn't quite true. The Cliff Swallows do come to Capistrano faithfully enough each spring to nest but their actual arrival dates are as variable as those elsewhere.

One of the most familiar and widespread members of the family is the bird the British know as The Swallow. The French and Germans refer to it as the Chimney Swallow, and

TREE SWALLOW
Iridoprocne bicolor
Temperate North America 5½ in.

ROUGH-WINGED SWALLOW
Stelgidopteryx ruficollis
Southern Canada to Argentina 5½ in.

BARN SWALLOW
Hirundo rustica
Holarctic; Eurasia, North America 7½ in.

we call it the Barn Swallow, as do the Dutch and Norwegians. It breeds throughout the North Temperate Zone, in both North America and Eurasia. North American Barn Swallows are slightly smaller than the European subspecies; their underparts are usually washed with brown, and the dark band across the chest has a break in its center. North American Barn Swallows winter in South America; the European subspecies travel to Africa, and the Asiatic populations migrate to Malaya and the Philippines. Close relatives of the Barn Swallow are resident in the Old World tropics; some nest in the South Temperate Zone and winter northward, among them the Welcome Swallow of Australia.

Throughout their extensive range the Barn Swallows and their kin (the genus *Hirundo*) nest in close association with man, and have done so since the dawn of history. Written records of them go back to early Greek civilization. In North America, they favor barns and sheds, as their name implies, and plaster their open cup of mud to the top or sides of rough-hewn rafters. European birds pick similar sites on outbuildings, but nest inside chimneys more often than their relatives elsewhere do. In Korea and Japan a swallow nesting on one's house is a sign of good luck, and the rice farmers encourage the birds by nailing small shelves for them under the eaves of their thatched roofs. The spread of man has doubtless increased the population of these swallows by providing nesting sites where none existed previously. Before man built houses and barns, the Barn Swallows apparently nested on cliff ledges or on sheltered tree branches, where very few still nest today.

Barn Swallows show strong faithfulness to their nesting territory and return year after year to the same site, often to the same nest. Occasionally they renovate the old nest; more often they build a completely new one near it. Both sexes work together, bringing little pellets of mud in their bills which they plaster in place and strengthen with grass and straw. The usual clutch is 4 or 5 white eggs, rarely 3 or 6. Incubation is entirely by the female, and the male usually sleeps beside the nest at night. He occasionally sits on the eggs during the female's absence by day, but he is unable to keep them at the proper temperature, for he lacks the brood patch—the bare space on the belly amply supplied with blood vessels—that incubating birds use to warm the eggs. Incubation takes 14 to 16 days, depending on the attentiveness of the female to her task. As in all weak-legged species that must be able to fly well on leaving the nest, the fledging period is comparatively long, from 20 to 24 days. The young usually return to roost at the nest for the first few nights after leaving.

Barn Swallows frequently rear a second brood and occasionally a third. The later clutches are usually smaller than the first—2 to 4 instead of 4 to 5 eggs. The young of the first brood usually stay in the vicinity, and often help the parents feed the later young. Adults not otherwise engaged or those that have lost their own broods frequently help feed the young in nearby nests. Banding studies have shown that young returning to breed for the first time nest a week or two later than older birds, and that third clutches are laid only by the oldest pairs. Barn Swallows are surprisingly long-lived—16 years is the record set by a Swallow banded in Britain.

Another mud-nest builder is the common House Martin of Eurasia, a small green-backed, white-bellied swallow much like our Tree Swallow. This species plasters its mud cups under house eaves, leaving a narrow entrance at one edge. Originally House Martins were cliff nesters. Large colonies of them still nest on rocky cliffs in the Japan Alps, just as their ancestors have done for ages, and often in unbelievable numbers. The Japanese value them as a tourist attraction, and establish colonies at large resort hotels by taking young birds from their nests and rearing them by hand where they want the birds to settle. These young birds migrate southward with their kind in late summer, and return in spring to the place where they were reared, not where they were hatched.

Other mud-nest builders among the swallows are the Cliff Swallow of Capistrano fame and the similar Red-rumped, or Mosque, Swallow of south temperate Eurasia. These birds build retort-shaped nests like a bottle lying on its side, with a small round entrance through the neck. They plaster them under the eaves of buildings, including temples and mosques in the Orient.

Many swallows are cavity nesters. Typical of this group is the Tree Swallow, common throughout most of temperate North America. The Tree Swallow's normal nesting site is a hole in a tree, either a natural cavity or one made and abandoned by woodpeckers, which the birds line first with grasses and then with feathers. Such sites are not too plentiful, and the Tree Swallow's numbers have always been limited by available nesting places rather than by food supply. Populations of Tree Swallows can readily be built up by supplying them suitable housing. The erection of bird boxes has encouraged their steady increase, and they have become one of the commonest bird-box occupants in North America.

One of the most popular bird-box users is the Purple

Martin, largest of the American swallows, and one of the few members of the family in which the sexes differ markedly. The Purple Martin will nest in colonies and use houses divided into compartments. Long before the arrival of the white man, the southeastern Indians hung gourds on poles for them, a practice still widely continued in the South today. A South American relative, the Brown-chested Martin, commonly uses the abandoned nests of ovenbirds and has been known to appropriate occupied ones.

Despite the site fidelity shown by all swallows to their nesting places and their strong territorial sense, many cases have been recorded of swallows nesting on moving vehicles—boats, trains, autos, tractors. I remember the pair of Gray-breasted Martins that occupied a bird box tacked to the taffrail of a little river steamer in British Guiana long ago. These birds stayed faithfully with the boat and successfully reared brood after brood as it went its weekly rounds up and down the Essequibo River, a round trip of 180 miles.

The simplest of swallow nests are those of the burrowing species, typified by the widespread Bank Swallow, which breeds circumpolarly around the Northern Hemisphere, and is called the Sand Martin abroad. Bank Swallows nest in colonies in vertical clay or sand banks, frequently along rivers. They dig horizontal tunnels 2 to 3 feet deep near the top of the bank, chipping the dirt free with their bills and scraping it out with their feet. They line the nesting chamber at its end with grass stalks, rootlets, and small sticks, and make a padded bed of feathers for their 4 to 5 white eggs.

The Rough-winged Swallow, so called because of the serrated web of its outer primaries, is another tunnel nester, but unlike the Bank Swallow, the Rough-winged does not nest in colonies, though several pairs may nest fairly near one another where conditions are favorable. A group of African swallows of the genus *Psalidoprocne* are also called Rough-wings. These birds live along forest edges and in open jungle clearings, and tunnel their nests into the banks of streams and into the walls of pitfalls the natives dig for big game. Most of these tropical species lay only two eggs.

The temperate zone Swallows are among the earliest of fall migrants. As soon as nesting duties are over in summer, the birds start gathering in large flocks, often in thousands, and take their departure southward late in summer or very early in the fall, moving by day and feeding as they go. Large mixed flocks of several species together can often be seen swooping over waterways, marshes, or fields where insects are plentiful, or resting on telegraph wires. Reedy marshes are favorite night roosts for the migrating flocks.

This was doubtless responsible for the medieval European belief that swallows were one of the "seven sleepers." People with no knowledge of far-off Africa, where the European swallows winter, thought the birds hibernated like frogs or turtles in the marsh ooze. This belief persisted well into the 19th century. Naturalists investigating reports of swallows found hibernating in the marshes invariably found dead ones, killed by starvation or cold. Though some birds do hibernate

male   female

PURPLE MARTIN
Progne subis
Temperate North America   8 in.

(goatsuckers), and others become torpid during a cold wet spell and recover (hummingbirds), this phenomenon has never been demonstrated conclusively in any of the swallows.

Occasionally swallows delay their mass autumn departure until early cold snaps clear the air of flying insects. The Tree Swallows are often caught off their guard in this manner on Cape Cod, Massachusetts, in October and November. The birds then may be seen hovering over the bayberry bushes along the coastal moors, stoking up on the waxy fruit.

Africa is the home of an aberrant swallow, the African River Martin, sometimes put in a family of its own because of its complete bronchial rings. This large black swallow has a red beak and red eyes. It nests on the sandy shoals exposed when the Congo River is low during the dry season, often in colonies of several hundred pairs, and lays its three eggs at the end of a burrow dug slanting down from the surface. When the rains come and the river rises the birds move southwestward and spend the wet season in coastal marshes.

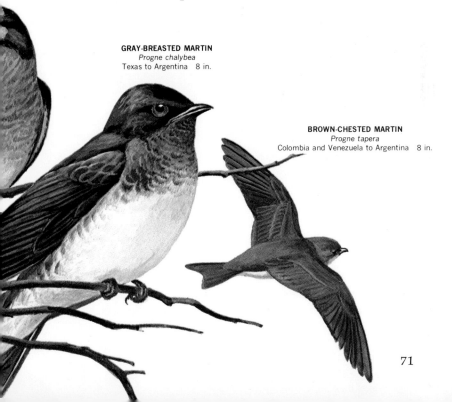

GRAY-BREASTED MARTIN
Progne chalybea
Texas to Argentina   8 in.

BROWN-CHESTED MARTIN
Progne tapera
Colombia and Venezuela to Argentina   8 in.

71

CUCKOO-SHRIKES
AND MINIVETS

PASSERIFORMES   CAMPEPHAGIDAE

Cuckoo-shrike is an unfortunate name for this group of Old
World birds. While some of them resemble shrikes and show
vague similarities to cuckoos, they are not related to either
family. More fitting is their family title, Campephagidae,
which means "caterpillar eater." Actually the cuckoo-shrikes
are rather primitive insect-eaters of uncertain antecedents
and relationships, perhaps distantly allied to the Old World
flycatchers. Their distribution is Africa and the warmer parts
of Asia from India northward to Manchuria and Japan, southward to Australia, and eastward to Samoa.

The 70 members of the family are small- to medium-sized
arboreal birds, 5 to 14 inches long. Family characteristics are
a stoutish down-curved bill, notched and hooked at the tip;
nostrils partly hidden by short bristles; pointed wings with
10 primaries, the outermost shortened; tail long, graduated
or rounded; legs usually short; feet rather weak. Their plumage is soft and fluffy, and an outstanding feature is the dense
patch of thick, often light-colored feathers on the lower back.
These have large, stiff shafts and are so loosely attached they
probably function as a defense mechanism, as do the loose
feathers in certain pigeons and the easily shed tail of many
lizards.

Most cuckoo-shrikes are a rather plain gray, black, or white,
with barred underparts. The minivets are generally more
brightly colored in reds, yellows, and oranges. The sexes are
similar in a few species, but are usually unlike, the females
usually being duller, brown birds. All feed on insects, other
small animals and occasionally berries. Some species, particu-

larly the northern minivets, are migratory; the tropical and subtropical forms are essentially sedentary. Fairly conspicuous birds, they are often gregarious. When not nesting, small noisy flocks wander through the treetops, sometimes in company with other species of similar habits, such as flycatchers and orioles.

Breeding patterns, so far as known, are much alike throughout the family. Campephagid nests are typically shallow open cups on a horizontal branch or fork, built of twigs and grasses, often camouflaged with lichens and spider webs, and small for the size of the bird. The 2 to 5 eggs are white, green, or blue and usually blotched or speckled. Both sexes usually build the nest, incubate, and rear the young. In some species only the female incubates, but the male stands by and feeds her on the nest. The incubation period is 13 to 14 days in the smaller species. The nestlings of many cuckoo-shrikes are covered with a snowy white down, which is replaced before fledging by a juvenile plumage closely resembling that of the female.

Representative of the family are the 41 cuckoo-shrikes of the genus *Coracina;* these range widely from Africa through Malaya and Australia to the Solomons. About 8 to 13 inches in length, the Coracinas are often called "gray birds" from their predominant color, or "caterpillar shrikes" from their favorite food. Some are quite shrikelike in appearance, a few species even having the black mask through the eyes. In their undulating flight, alternating flurries of rapid wingbeats with short glides, they suggest cuckoos. They inhabit heavy forest, most often living in the treetops. Their voice range is limited to harsh churrs and whistles; they often call in flight, but their notes are seldom loud or far-carrying.

The several species of the nominate genus *Campephaga* are African. In this group the males are glossy black, some with patches of red or yellow on the shoulders, the females brownish. Several closely related African species (*Lobotos*) have fleshy lobes of yellow or orange at the corner of the mouth. The Wattled Cuckoo-shrike is called the Oriole

1 ROSY MINIVET
Pericrocotus roseus
Afghanistan to
southern China   8 in.

**2 RED-SHOULDERED
CUCKOO-SHRIKE**
Campephaga phoenicea
Africa south of the Sahara   8 in.

3 BARRED CUCKOO-SHRIKE
Coracina lineata
Australia and New Guinea
east to the Solomons   9½ in.

4 WHITE-WINGED TRILLER
Lalage sueurii
Java, Celebes, New Guinea,
Australia   7 in.

5 FLAMED MINIVET
Pericrocotus flammeus
India to the Philippines
and Borneo   9 in.

Cuckoo-shrike because it resembles a forest oriole in size and coloring.

Another well-marked group consists of the smaller (6- to 8-inch) cuckoo-shrikes known as trillers (*Lalage*) from the loud, clear whistling notes of the males when courting. Trillers range from southern Asia to Australia, the Philippines, and the western Pacific islands. The males are mostly black and white, the females brownish. The White-winged Triller of Australia is the only member of the family to molt twice a year. The male goes into an eclipse molt after the breeding season and assumes a brownish dress like that of the female which he discards for his marked black and white nuptial garb the following spring. In southern Australia the White-winged Triller is migratory.

Australia is also the home of the largest member of the family, and one of the most aberrant, the 14-inch Ground Cuckoo-shrike. While this species spends much of its time foraging on the ground, it nests like the rest of the family in trees, 30 feet or so up, and builds the usual small, shallow nest for its 2 to 3 brown-spotted green eggs. After fledging in November or December, the young remain with their parents and wander about the countryside in small flocks until September, when they scatter to breed.

The 10 minivets (*Pericrocotus*) are neat, slender birds with sharply pointed tails, and so different from the other campephagids that some ornithologists give them subfamily rank. Minivets are birds of the treetops, ranging throughout southern and eastern Asia from Afghanistan to Japan and southward to Malaysia and the Philippines. While they forage among the leaves and branches like the rest of the family, minivets frequently catch insects on the wing in flycatcher fashion. One of the larger and brighter species, the 8-inch Flamed Minivet, common from India to the Philippines, is quite gregarious. Noisy bands of 20 or more birds rove through the treetops in the high green jungle. They are conspicuous both for their gay, striking colors and their endless melodious chattering.

The northernmost species, the Ashy Minivet, is patterned more somberly, like the cuckoo-shrikes, in grays, black, and white. In Japan and Korea it vies with the swallows as a herald of spring, arriving from the south in April. A slender, gray bird with long wings and graduated tail, it flies high in the sky and proclaims the season with a pleasant, far-carrying note cool as the peal of a bell. It nests in the deciduous woodlands of the foothills, building a small, delicate, thin-walled nest of lichens, mosses, pine needles, and small twigs cleverly fastened together with spider webs. Its normal clutch is 4 to 5 bluish-gray eggs spotted heavily with purplish brown at the large end. Incubation is by the female alone. She raises but a single brood each summer.

DRONGOS

PASSERIFORMES   DICRURIDAE

The 20 species of drongos are Old World arboreal birds found throughout Africa south of the Sahara and in Asia from India and China southward to northern Australia and eastward to the Solomon Islands. They live in deep forests, in wooded savannas, and in cultivated lands and gardens, and may be found from sea level up to perhaps 10,000 feet. A few species are migratory.

Drongos range from the size of a starling to that of a large jay. Their stout arched bills are slightly hooked and notched, and prominent bristles shield the nostrils. Their legs are short, their feet strong. Except for the highly variable Gray Drongo of southeastern Asia and the Whitebellied Drongo of India and Ceylon, drongos are black with bright metallic sheens of green to purple. A few species have white patches on the head or underparts. Many have a crest, or ornamental plumes on the head or neck, and most have a rather long, deeply forked tail. In some, the outer tail feathers are greatly elongated, curved, and variously ornamented. The Great Racket-tailed Drongo of the Indian and Malayan forests has wire-like outer tail feathers tipped with miniature flags which extend a foot beyond the rest of the tail and almost double the length of the bird.

Drongos are conspicuous birds fond of sitting in the open on exposed dead branches and electric wires, where they watch for passing insects. They pounce on the insects ferociously and carry them back to the perch to eat. Large prey, such as locusts or grasshoppers, they hold down with one foot and tear to pieces with their beak before swallowing. Some species like to hang around cattle, feeding on the insects disturbed by their passage; others accompany troops of monkeys through the treetops for the same purpose. Most drongos are fairly noisy; their calls are varied and harsh. Some have melodious, attractive songs as well, and a few mimic other species of birds with considerable skill.

The relationships and systematic position of the drongos are uncertain. Kinship to the shrikes, the orioles, the jays, and the birds of paradise has been proposed, and to all of these the drongos show some resemblances. Behaviorally they seem closest to the Old World flycatchers. The most recent revision of the group unites 19 species, all with 10-feathered tails, in the single genus *Dicrurus*. The 20th species, the diminutive Mountain Drongo (*Chaetorhynchus*) of New Guinea, has 12 tail feathers and strongly resembles a flycatcher. This jungle dweller is considered the most primitive of the drongos.

Throughout their wide Old World range the drongos are famed for their pugnacity and for their aggressive protection of their nesting territory. Like the American Kingbirds, they promptly attack any and every large bird that trespasses on their domain, and no predator cares to arouse their fury. Hawks, eagles, and crows flee before their aerial onslaught, though in fair combat any of these large predators should be more than a match for the much smaller drongos. Congo tribes call the Velvet-mantled Drongo "Nkandongoe," which roughly translated means "angry leopard." The name drongo, by which all members of the family are known, is the native Malagasy name for the Crested Drongo of northern Madagascar.

The commonest and most conspicuous drongo of India and southeastern Asia is a 12-inch shiny black bird with a forked tail. It is called the King Crow, not because of its black coloring, but because it is the master of these traditional nest robbers and drives them and other predators larger than itself away fearlessly. Drongos seem to limit their attacks to potentially dangerous animals and birds, a trait which less aggressive species of equal and smaller size take advantage of. A tree with a King Crow's nest may also shelter nests of orioles, doves, and other gentle species enjoying safety from marauders because of the drongos' presence.

Comparatively little is known of the breeding behavior of the drongos. Most of them build a small, fragile, saucer-like nest, usually in a forked branch fairly high up. They lay anywhere from 2 to 5 (usually 3 to 4) eggs, which may be pure white or speckled with browns and grays. Incubation is believed largely by the female, though the male may assist at times. Both sexes cooperate in rearing the young. Drongos are frequently parasitized by cuckoos, and one Asiatic cuckoo, called the Drongo-cuckoo (*Surniculus*), looks so much like a drongo it is often mistaken for one, which is thought may facilitate its parasitizing of drongo nests.

OLD WORLD ORIOLES

PASSERIFORMES   ORIOLIDAE

The English word "oriole" stems from the Latin *aureolus,* meaning golden or yellow, and was originally applied most appropriately to the brilliant Golden Oriole that breeds widely throughout Europe and western Asia, wintering southward into Africa. This bird is the only European representative of a family of 28 species of brightly colored Old World birds, essentially tropical and subtropical in distribution. They range widely throughout Africa, southern Asia, and the East Indies to New Guinea and eastern Australia. These "true" orioles are 10-primaried birds allied anatomically to the crow and jay group, and are not related to the birds we call orioles in the New World. Though the American orioles resemble the true orioles superficially, they have only nine primaries. They are of Western Hemisphere origin and closely allied to the tanagers.

The Old World orioles are all forest dwellers that live, feed, and breed in the treetops. Starling-sized birds from 8 to 12 inches in length, all have 12 tail feathers and short, fine bristles concealing the nostrils. Throughout the genus *Oriolus,* which embraces all but three members of the family, the sexes differ in color. The males are predominantly yellow and black, and most of them have reddish bills. The females are much duller, usually greenish, and the young in their first juvenile plumage are even drabber, though frequently streaked and speckled with brown.

Orioles are strong, fast fliers, and have a characteristic undulating flight reminiscent of that of the woodpeckers. Despite their brilliant colors, the males are far more often heard than seen in their leafy treetop habitat. Their call notes are loud, flutey whistles, and most species have a pleasant, melodious song as well. Some of the tropical forms, notably the Black-headed Oriole of Africa, are excellent mimics and include startlingly accurate imitations of the songs of other species in their courtship repertoires.

The 24 species of the genus *Oriolus* are essentially a tropical and subtropical group, with their greatest development in diversity of species in the jungles of central Africa, southern Asia, and Indonesia. From this center of distribution several forms have spread into more temperate regions to breed during the clement summer months, migrating back to warmer climes during the colder parts of the year. Typical of such species are the Golden Oriole of Europe and its eastern Asiatic counterpart, the Black-naped Oriole, which breeds northward to Korea and Manchuria and winters southward to Malaya and Indonesia. These birds are highly regared as songsters in their northern breeding grounds, and their appearance in late spring, with bright colors suggestive of exotic warmer lands, is welcomed as the surest sign that summer has really arrived.

Orioles are not gregarious and are usually encountered singly or in pairs, foraging through the treetops. They eat many kinds of insects, particularly during the breeding season, and are among the few birds that consume quantities of woolly caterpillars, which they first pound against a branch to remove the fuzz. Later they augment this diet with fruits, showing a fondness for cherries, mulberries, currants, figs, and loquats which does not endear them to orchardists.

These orioles weave intricate cup-shaped nests of grasses and strips of bark, usually between the forks of a high horizontal branch, slinging the structure like a hammock attached firmly to branches on each side. They lay 2 to 5 eggs (usually 3 to 4), which are commonly white, more or less heavily speckled with brown or black. In the northern species both sexes build the nest and share the incubation and rearing duties. In the few tropical species that have been adequately studied, incubation is largely by the female. The male feeds her on the nest. In most orioles the incubation period is 14 to 15 days, and the young remain in the nest another two weeks before they take flight.

Somewhat aberrant members of the oriole family are the two Fig Birds (*Sphecotheres*) of eastern and northern Australia and New Guinea. The Fig Birds differ from the *Oriolus* group in having the bill slightly down-curved and the lores and the eye region bare of feathers. These handsome birds also differ somewhat from the nominate group in habits, mainly in being far more gregarious. They tend to travel in small, noisy flocks and, as their name implies, feed largely on

BLACK-NAPED ORIOLE
Oriolus chinensis
India and Manchuria to the Philippines
and Celebes 9 in.

MAROON ORIOLE
Oriolus traillii
Himalayas to Formosa 9 in.

YELLOW FIGBIRD
Sphecotheres flaviventris
Northern Australia 10 in.

OLD WORLD ORIOLES 81

fruits and berries. Their nesting habits are similar to those of other orioles, except that they usually lay but three eggs, which are predominantly greenish and brown in color, heavily spotted with reddish or brownish markings. Also classified tentatively with the orioles is the little-known Kinkimavo (*Tylas*) of the Madagascar forests. Recent studies suggest the Fairy Bluebirds, now classified with the leafbirds, may be aberrant orioles.

CROWS AND JAYS

PASSERIFORMES   CORVIDAE

Among the 102 species assigned to the Corvidae are some of the world's most familiar birds. Possessors of conspicuous personalities, bold, active, noisy, and aggressive, the crows ravens, rooks, jackdaws, jays, and their kindred have always claimed man's interest and attention. The distinctive vernacular names he has given them are household words in many tongues. No other group of birds has earned for itself a more prominent place in legend, folklore, literature, and common everyday speech.

Though best developed in the Northern Hemisphere, the crow family is almost world-wide in distribution, absent only from Antarctica, New Zealand, certain oceanic islands, and southern South America. Ornithologists generally divide the crow family into two subfamilies, the larger, more somber crows (Corvinae) and the smaller, more colorful jays (Garrulinae). The crows have relatively long, pointed wings and short tails, the jays shorter, rounded wings and longer tails. The structural differences between the two are not always well marked. Several genera are difficult to assign positively to either subfamily.

As a family the corvids are a generalized, relatively unspecialized group of considerable age, evolutionarily speaking, and probably closest to the ancestral stock from which over the ages they and their more specialized relatives, the orioles, birds of paradise, bowerbirds, and others, have developed. Technically they are diagnosed as medium- to large-sized, 10-primaried oscine birds with strong, unnotched bills, the nostrils usually covered with forward-directed bristles, the legs and feet large and strong, the tarsus scaled in front, smooth behind, and terminating in a ridge. Typically inhabitants of forests, brushlands, and grasslands, crows and jays are seldom finicky in their choice of food. Many will eat almost anything they can swallow, animal or vegetable, and so are able to survive changing conditions in a variety of habitats. At the same time some groups have strangely limited distributions, apparently restricted by some particular environmental factor. Several species have widely disrupted ranges.

COMMON CROW
Corvus brachyrhynchos
Temperate North America   21 in.

From its present distribution the family is thought to have arisen in what are now the northern temperate and subtropical portions of the Old World and to have spread from there into the rest of its present range. (Corvids left their fossil remains in Miocene deposits in Europe 25 million years ago.) The great development of the jay subfamily in Central and South America suggests an ancestor's early invasion of the New World, possibly in mid-Tertiary time. The absence of jays from Africa south of the Sahara suggests a later Old World conquest by jays from the Western Hemisphere.

The crow subfamily seems to have reached the New World considerably later than the jays, for its members have pushed southward only as far as Honduras, and are absent from South America. Yet the crows are more aggressive and more adaptable than the jays, and are stronger fliers. They have established themselves in many more island regions—the West Indies, Australia, the Philippines, and other smaller Pacific islands in which jays are unknown. Crows have been in the West Indies long enough to develop four distinct though similar species, one each on Cuba, Hispaniola, Puerto Rico, and Jamaica. Pleistocene deposits in the West Indies have yielded bones of still two more crow species, either or both of which may have been ancestral to the present forms.

Possibly no bird or group of birds is better known to more people than the crows of the nominate genus *Corvus*. The Common Crow, which is widespread in North America, the very similar Carrion Crow of temperate Eurasia, the House Crow of India, the Jungle Crow of eastern and southeastern Asia, the Pied Crow of South Africa, and some 26 other members of the genus are large, black, black and gray, or black and white birds with raucous voices. All are called "crows" wherever English is spoken and they all say "crow," "craw," "caw," or "krahe."

The crows are the largest-bodied of the passerine birds, and the largest of them is the Raven, which measures 26 inches from tip of bill to tip of tail. (The Raven is exceeded in length by the Ribbon-tailed Bird of Paradise, by the lyrebirds

BLACK-BILLED MAGPIE
Pica pica
Eurasia,
western North America 18 in.

AZURE-WINGED MAGPIE
Cyanopica cyanus
Spain, eastern China, Japan 13 in.

GREEN MAGPIE
Cissa chinensis
Himalayas to Indochina,
Borneo, Sumatra 14 in.

of Australia, and by the handsome, slender 28-inch Magpie Jay of Central America, all of which have smaller bodies.) The Raven is the most widespread as well as the largest species in the family, for it occurs, or did until the last

century or so, in practically all the arctic and temperate Northern Hemisphere. The Raven is difficult to distinguish in the field from other black corvines other than by its more guttural croaking calls. Its slightly larger size, heavier bill, and more pointed, shaggier throat feathers are hard to discern at a distance. The Raven has not fared so well in competition with mankind as some of its smaller relatives. It is now found only in the wilder, uninhabited parts of its range, and is most common today north of the tree line.

A singular attribute of most crows is their ability to coexist with man. Their adaptability and their boldness and sagacity, coupled with their extensive dietary range—they are practically omnivorous—have enabled them to live and thrive in country radically altered by man's activities. In agricultural regions crows are a mixed blessing, for their inroads on sprouting grain are partly offset by their consumption of enormous numbers of injurious insects and larvae.

Crows are widely credited with being the most "intelligent" of all birds. Though much of the evidence supporting this is blatantly anthropomorphic, there is no question that crows do have mental qualities of a high order. Experiments with captive crows show they have considerable learning ability, that they can count up to three or four and learn to associate various noises and symbols with food. That crows have a language of their own and that their calls have recognizable meanings (as indeed do those of all birds) has long been known. Before the days of modern behavior studies and scientific analyses of bird noises with hi-fi equipment and sound spectrographs, most country boys knew the difference between the various crow calls: the loud, clear assembly "caaw," the rapid "ca-ca-ca-ca" of alarm, and the excited scolding when mobbing an owl. Crows have some imitative skill, and with patience captive ones can be taught to say a few words, but they are not as good at it as mynahs and parrots.

The best proof of crows' intelligence is their adaptability to change and their success in withstanding constant persecution. Almost everywhere man is against them, and in North America they have never been protected. Their well-known penchant for the eggs and young of other species turns sentimental bird lovers against them, and their forays on nesting waterfowl and game birds make every hunter their enemy. Still they manage to survive and prosper—despite wholesale dynamiting of their winter roosts that slaughters thousands at a time.

Nor is the crows' rate of reproduction abnormally high. They are typically single-brooded, and the clutch varies from 3 to 5 (occasionally 6) greenish eggs heavily spotted with brown. Most of the family are tree nesters; the raven and a few others often nest on cliffs. All build substantial open nests of twigs and sticks. Incubation is entirely by the female, who sits closely and is fed on the nest by the male. Incubation in the Common Crow takes 18 to 19 days, and the fledging period is about 3 weeks.

A distinctive Eurasian member of the genus *Corvus* is the slightly smaller Rook, whose habit of nesting in large colonies gives us the term rookery for any such assemblage regardless of species (even breeding colonies of seals are called rookeries). Another still smaller species is the black and white or black and gray Jackdaw. Other genera in the crow subfamily include two other fairly well-known northern birds, the choughs and the nutcrackers.

The choughs inhabit rocky heights in Europe and southwestern Asia. These rather small corvids are glossy black like most of the group, but are distinctive in their thinner, pointed, and strongly down-curved bills, which are bright red in the Common Chough and yellow in the Alpine Chough, the only two species in the genus *Pyrrhocorax*. The Common Chough nests on ledges along inaccessible sea cliffs. The Alpine Chough prefers ledges in the mountains. Both are noted for their aerial acrobatics. Individually and in flocks they perform all sorts of flight evolutions around their cliffs, wheeling and dashing back and forth, climbing high and diving like a plummet with closed wings, even turning somersaults—all seemingly for the fun of it.

Nutcrackers are jay-sized inhabitants of mountain forests in northern Eurasia and western North America. The Nutcracker of Eurasia is a brownish bird handsomely spangled with white (the Japanese call him the star crow); Clark's Nutcracker (discovered by the Lewis and Clark expedition in 1805) is a pale-gray bird whose black wings and tail have white patches that show conspicuously in flight. Nutcrackers prefer evergreen forests, but are often found above the timber line in the mountains. Omnivorous like most crows and jays, they eat all sorts of insects, grubs, and the eggs and young of other birds, but their principal food is nuts and seeds. They are adept at hacking pine cones open, holding a cone with one foot and hewing it apart with pickax strokes of their strong bills. The nutcrackers are notorious food-storers. They make caches of pine cones and hazel nuts in summer and fall, and show a phenomenal ability to return to the exact spot to dig out their supply even when it is covered with snow. They are not infallible, however, and nuts and cones nutcrackers bury and fail to retrieve help reforest barren mountain regions.

The jays are a more varied group than the crows, and much more colorful in appearance. The subfamily is exceptionally well diversified in Central and South America where no less than 28 of the 32 New World species occur, and in south-eastern Asia where more than half of the Old World forms live, including some of the most brilliantly colored members of the family, such as the Chinese Green, the Ceylon Blue, and the Red-billed Blue magpies.

TURQUOISE JAY
Cyanolyca turcosa
Andes, Colombia to Peru   13 in.

EURASIAN JAY
Garrulus glandarius
Temperate Eurasia   13 in.

BLUE JAY
Cyanocitta cristata
Eastern North America   12 in.

The somewhat more specialized feeding habits and nesting behavior of a number of jays and their strangely restricted and disrupted distribution patterns suggest that the group may be an earlier, more ancient one than the crows. Small colonies of the Azure-winged Magpie, for instance, are woodland residents of extreme eastern Asia and Japan. The species suddenly reappears on the other side of Eurasia in the highlands of Spain. The North American Scrub Jay shows a similar relict distribution. This species breaks into a number of races on our west coast from Washington to southern Mexico, and is absent from the rest of the continent except for a population resident in the scrublands of central Florida.

Widest ranging and most familiar of the Old World species is the Common Jay, found in temperate Eurasian woodlands from the British Isles to Japan. Although the Common Jay is fairly omnivorous and fond of all sorts of animal food, its diet is almost three-fourths vegetable matter. Acorns are its mainstay, and its distribution closely coincides with that of the oak trees that produce them. In much of its range it is regarded as a game bird and shot for sport and food. In England and parts of Europe gamekeepers kill it whenever they can because of its fondness for the eggs and young of game birds. That the Common Jay still manages to remain fairly plentiful throughout its extensive range speaks highly for its adaptability and reproductive powers. It is single-brooded, but lays from 5 to 7 eggs. It nests in trees and builds a well-constructed and fairly bulky open cup of twigs usually lined with grass. As in most jays, but not in crows, the male shares the incubation duties. The incubation period is 16 to 17 days. Fledging takes another 19 to 20 days.

The Common Jay's New World counterpart is the cocky Blue Jay of temperate North America east of the Rockies. Essentially a woodland species fond of open forest, the Blue Jay has become a common resident of the parks and suburbs of most North American cities.

Most corvids tend to be residents and few have well-marked migrations. They do wander considerably after the breeding season, often in small flocks. Banding has shown that the Blue Jay seldom travels more than a few hundred miles. Blue Jays also are fairly long-lived; a number of banded individuals have lived 10 to 12 years, the oldest to date, 15 years. Though length of life is roughly a corollary of size, with larger animals living longer, the oldest wild crow on the banding records was 13 years old when killed. However, crows have lived in captivity beyond 20 years.

Northernmost of the jays are those of the circumpolar genus *Perisoreus,* resident in the boreal birch and conifer forests. The American species, widely known as the Canada Jay, is a mischievous bird familiar to all north woods travelers. The Siberian Jay is similar in appearance and habits, but browner in color.

The only jay species common to both hemispheres is the Black-billed Magpie, which ranges across Eurasia and into western North America. Its only close relative, the Yellow-billed Magpie, is limited to the valleys and foothills of California west of the High Sierras. Conspicuous black and white birds with very long tails, these magpies are more like the crows in certain aspects, particularly their nesting behavior, and some students consider them intermediate between the two subfamilies. Birds of semi-open country, Black-billed Magpies are thoroughly at home in Old World farmlands. They usually go about in small flocks, are as noisy and mischievous as any member of the family, and are one of the most notorious thieves, prone to pick up all sorts of bright objects and carry them away. Their fondness for the eggs of other species has led to their persecution by gamekeepers, but their diet is as varied as that of most corvines. They hang about cattle and other large ruminants more than other corvids do, and may even be seen perched on a cow's back.

Magpies make a large bulky stick nest from 1 to 3 feet in diameter, usually in the trunk fork of a deciduous tree. The nests are conspicuous features of the landscape wherever the birds are plentiful. Nest-building is part of the magpies' courtship, the male bringing the material, the female arranging it. The tremendous nests are often used and added to year after year. Incubation by the female alone is one of their crowlike idiosyncracies. This takes 17 to 18 days, and fledging of the young, which the male helps feed, lasts another 22 to 27 days.

WATTLEBIRDS

PASSERIFORMES   CALLAEIDAE

Three distinctive New Zealand forest birds, each placed in a separate genus, form this small family—the extinct Huia, and the still extant but rare Saddleback and Wattled Crow. All three have rather weak wings, large, strong legs and feet, and large fleshy wattles at the corner of the jaws, bluish gray in the Wattled Crow, yellow to orange in the others. They are believed offshoots of the primitive crowlike stock that produced the bowerbirds, birds of paradise, mudnest-builders, and bellmagpies.

Most interesting of the three species was the Huia. The whitish bills of the male and female were so different that the first specimens to reach Europe were considered distinct species. The male's beak was stout, straight, and chisel-like; the female's was longer, thinner, and gracefully down-curved. Pairs of these large, glossy-black birds hunted together on or

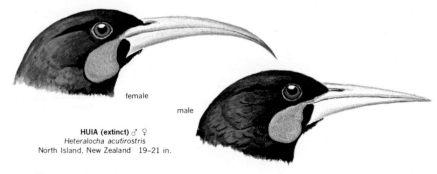

female

male

HUIA (extinct) ♂ ♀
Heteralocha acutirostris
North Island, New Zealand   19–21 in.

near the ground in deep forests for wood-boring grubs, the male chiseling away the bark and wood to expose the borings, the female probing into the holes to extract the grubs. The Maoris valued the Huias' white-tipped tail feathers, which they used in chiefs' ceremonial headdresses. Living Huias have not been reported reliably since 1907. Overzealous hunting by the Maoris and by European collectors of museum specimens has been blamed for the Huia's extinction, but destruction of its primeval forest habitat was a far more important factor. The Maoris hunted it for years before Europeans arrived without seriously affecting its numbers. A recent survey showed only 67 specimens traceable in museums of the world today, and it is doubtful the Europeans ever collected more than two or three times that number.

The Saddleback, or Tieke as the Maoris call it, is also glossy black, but has a conspicuous chestnut back. The sexes are alike and both have black, straight, pointed bills. Saddlebacks are smaller than the Huia, about 10 inches long. They are poor fliers but flit from branch to branch through the forest understory and hop on the ground. Their food is mainly insects, also some fuits and flower nectar. They build a cup-shaped nest deep in a tree-fern stem or in rock crevices, and lay 2 to 3 brownish-gray eggs heavily spotted with brown which are incubated 20 to 21 days. Saddlebacks now survive only on tiny Hen Island, less than 2,000 acres in extent, about 9 miles off Whangarie on the northeast coast of North Island. They are rigidly protected and at last reports (1964) the colony of perhaps 1,000 pairs was thriving.

SADDLEBACK
Creadion carunculatus
New Zealand   10 in.

WATTLED CROW
Callaeas cinerea
New Zealand   17–18 in.

The Wattled Crow, or Kokako, a large blue-gray, jaylike bird with a short, heavy, down-curved beak, was plentiful a century ago but is now restricted to the few stands of highland forest remaining on the main islands. It flies weakly, but moves through the trees and over the ground in long hops, aided partly by its wings. It lives more on fruit and berries than the other two species, and its song is considered the most beautiful of all New Zealand bird music. The Kokako builds an untidy open nest of twigs lined with bark and moss, usually 20 to 30 feet up in a tree. The clutch is 2 to 3 spotted grayish eggs. The incubation period is unknown, but the young remain in the nest 4 weeks.

MUDNEST BUILDERS

PASSERIFORMES   GRALLINIDAE

The four members of this odd little antipodean family all build similar nests—deep open bowls of mud strengthened with hair, feathers, and grass, usually on a high horizontal branch. All are somewhat gregarious, fly rather weakly, and have peculiar jumping gaits both on the ground and in trees. They live in open woodlands, along lake shores and stream banks, and in marshes and cultivated areas; they are usually found near water.

The mudlarks (*Grallina*) are the smallest members of the family. The 11-inch Australian Mudlark, also called Magpie-lark or Pee-wit, is a graceful, boldly black and white, rather tame inhabitant of open stream banks, lake shores, and marshes. The slightly smaller but similarly colored Papuan Mudlark is the least gregarious member of the family, and lives solitarily or in pairs along rushing streams in the forested mountains of western New Guinea. The Australian species gathers in flocks of up to 500 birds in winter, but the pairs establish individual nesting territories in spring. Magpie-larks are believed to pair for life, and each pair maintains the same nesting ground, which may be as large as 15 or 20 acres, year after year. Both sexes defend it, and sing antiphonally while courting. When one bird sings the first two syllables of the song, a shrill whistled "te-he," its mate immediately finishes the remaining "pee-o-wit" in perfect synchronization. Mudlarks lay four heavily spotted white eggs and are multibrooded. Their peculiar mud nests are often washed away by heavy rains. They are thought to build a new one for each brood. They feed on insects and small aquatic life, and as they consume quantities of mollusks that are the alternate hosts of sheep-infecting flukes, they are regarded as highly beneficial birds.

The Apostle Bird, or Gray Jumper (*Struthidea*), of eastern Australia has earned its two unusual common names. First, it travels about the open forest and farmlands in small flocks of about a dozen birds; second, it hops rather quaintly in long leaps over the ground and from branch to branch while uttering harsh, grating cries. Dark-gray birds the size of a large jay, Apostle Birds feed largely on the ground on insects and seeds. They are reported to nest communally.

The fourth and largest member of the family is the glossy black White-winged Chough (*Corcorax*), also a resident of eastern Australia. Like the Apostle Bird, the White-winged Chough goes about in small flocks and feeds mostly on the ground on insects, but also eats fruits and berries. It flies with slow wingbeats, and its white wing patches are conspicuous in flight. When disturbed it hops off through the trees in a series of long jumps from branch to branch. It also is reported to be multibrooded and a communal nester, three birds usually combining to build the typical mud nest, in which several females may lay. How many eggs each lays is unknown, but as many as eight have been found in a nest. Like those of the other members of the family, the eggs are whitish and spotted with brown.

AUSTRALIAN BUTCHERBIRDS AND BELLMAGPIES

PASSERIFORMES   CRACTICIDAE

This small group of 10 Australian and Papuan birds shows strong affinities to the crows and jays and probably developed from magpielike ancestors that became isolated in the Antipodes fairly early in Tertiary time.

The Gray Butcherbird, common and widespread throughout temperate Australia, is remarkably like the northern shrikes, and has the same habit of impaling insects, lizards, small birds, or rodents on thorns or hanging them on twigs to be eaten later. It uses the thorn or a convenient tree crotch to hold its prey firm while it tears it into small pieces.

Australians rate the butcherbirds, with their clear, mellow calls, among their finest songsters. The butcherbirds sing practically the year round, are noted for their duetting or antiphonal singing, and are also accomplished mimics.

Pairs of butcherbirds apparently stay mated and defend their territories throughout the year. The females take as active a part in this and in the singing courtship as do the males. They build untidy, crowlike nests of twigs lined with softer material in a tree fork, and lay 3 to 5 varicolored, heavily spotted eggs. Their incubation period is rather long for a passerine bird—23 days, followed by a fledging period of 25 to 26 days.

Bellmagpies, 14 to 20 inches in length, resemble magpies in their black and white coloring but have much shorter tails. All are fine singers and have ringing, gonglike calls that resound through the bush. The Gray Bellmagpie, the largest of the family, is disliked by orchardists for its fruit-eating, and by bird lovers for its fondness for the eggs and young of other birds. It also eats insects in quantity.

The Western Bellmagpie has territorial relationships unknown in any other bird, for it lives in clans of from 6 to 20 individuals of varying sex ratios that establish clan territories up to 100 acres in extent. Members of the clan remain within its boundaries throughout the year and defend the frontiers against incursions from neighboring clans. Individuals seem to be promiscuous, and the clan relationships are apparently somewhat communistic.

At mating time all the clan participates in a caroling songfest, which dies down during the incubation period. Nestbuilding and incubating are entirely by the females, but the males assist in feeding the young and in protecting them.

MAGPIE-LARK
Grallina cyanoleuca
Australia   11 in.

WHITE-WINGED CHOUGH
Corcorax melanorhamphus
Southeastern Australia   18 in.

Aggressive in defense of their nests, they attack all other species that approach, including humans. The nest is large and bowl-shaped, and usually placed high in a tree fork. Made of sticks and lined with finer grasses and leaves, a peculiar feature in its construction is the frequent use of heavy wire. One Western Bellmagpie's nest is reported to have weighed 13¾ pounds. It contained 286 pieces of miscellaneous wire, some of it barbed wire from stock fences, varying in length from 4 inches to 4 feet and totaling 338 feet.

GRAY BUTCHERBIRD
Cracticus torquatus
Australia and Tasmania   11 in.

CRESTLESS GARDENER ♂
Amblyornis inornatus
Western New Guinea 9 in.

SPOTTED BOWERBIRD ♂
Chlamydera maculata
Eastern Australia 11–12 in.

BOWERBIRDS

PASSERIFORMES   PTILONORHYNCHIDAE

The most remarkable characteristic of the 17 species of bower-birds is the extraordinary display grounds the males of most species build as part of their courtship. While a number of other birds establish special plots for courting and clear or modify them to suit their fancy (manakins, lyrebirds, and certain grouse are examples), none builds such elaborate structures as the bowerbirds. Some bowerbirds erect such large edifices it is hard to believe they are the work of one small bird. In fact the first ones seen by early explorers were thought to be playhouses built by native children.

Bowerbirds are so closely related to the birds of paradise that some students consider them subfamilies of the same family. The two groups have almost identical ranges—they are known only from New Guinea and northern Australia—and the structural differences separating them are not particularly well marked. They show minor divergences in palate structure and in the arrangement of the feather tracts, and differ in the relative length of the hind toe, which is

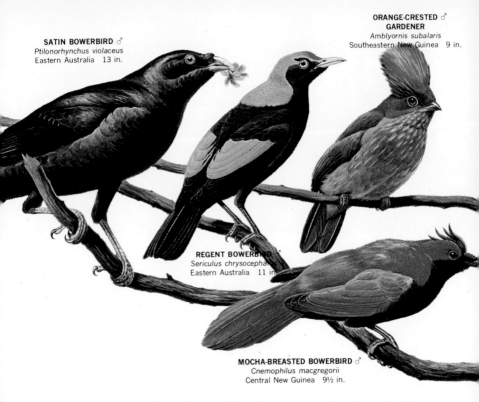

SATIN BOWERBIRD ♂
Ptilonorhynchus violaceus
Eastern Australia 13 in.

ORANGE-CRESTED ♂
GARDENER
Amblyornis subalaris
Southeastern New Guinea 9 in.

REGENT BOWERBIRD
Sericulus chrysocephalus
Eastern Australia 11 in.

MOCHA-BREASTED BOWERBIRD ♂
Cnemophilus macgregorii
Central New Guinea 9½ in.

always shorter than the middle front toe in the bowerbirds, but as long or longer in the birds of paradise. While the sexes are unlike in most bowerbirds, they are similar in the more primitive species. Some male bowerbirds are brilliantly colored, and a few have crests and elongated head feathers, but none has the distinctive gaudy plumes of the male birds of paradise. The outstanding difference between the two groups is their courtship behavior. Whereas male birds of paradise attract their mates by displaying their outrageously showy plumes, the male bowerbirds' forte is making their surroundings attractive. They have developed skills as architects and decorators found nowhere else below man in the animal kingdom. In their respective methods of display, the bowerbirds and the birds of paradise are unquestionably the most highly specialized wooers among all birds.

A noteworthy and curious aspect of bowerbirds' activities is that the male's skill as a builder is not used for nest construction. Each male builds his bower or stage by himself and performs there alone. The bower's sole function seems to be to attract a female and to stimulate her to mate, and mating takes place within it. After mating, the male takes no further part in the reproductive duties. The female goes off by herself and alone builds her shallow cup-shaped nest of twigs, lays and incubates her two eggs, and rears the young. While suspected, polygamy has not been proved in the bowerbirds.

Bowerbirds are classed for convenience into four groups according to their type of bower: those that build no bower, the stage makers, the maypole builders, and the avenue builders. The first group, considered the most primitive of the family, contains two species, the Green Catbird of eastern and northern Australia and the Aru Islands, and the congeneric White-throated Catbird of western New Guinea (both unrelated to American catbirds). These two species have feline mewing call notes and hissing, spitting alarm cries. In both species the sexes are alike. Catbirds have shorter, heavier, and stouter bills than the more highly developed bowerbirds, are more arboreal, and are seldom seen on the ground. Their food is fruit, berries, seeds, and some insects, mainly beetles. Beyond the fact that the males build no bower, little has been published about their breeding behavior. Whether or not the males assume more of the nesting and rearing duties than in the other species is unknown. The catbird nest is like that of the other bowerbirds, a cup-like structure of twigs, usually fairly high in a forest tree. The normal clutch is two cream-colored eggs.

The simplest bowers are those built by the three so-called stage makers, best known of which is the Toothed-billed Bowerbird of the scrubby highland forests of northeastern Australia. The sexes are similarly plain and protectively colored in this species—olive-brown above and streaked brown and white below. Both have deep sawlike notches near the tip of both upper and lower mandibles, with which the male cuts the leaves it uses to decorate its playground. This stage maker clears a space 3 to 5 feet in diameter on the ground in

BLACK-FACED ♂
GOLDEN BOWERBIRD
Sericulus aureus
New Guinea and
northern Australia 10 in.

SPOTTED BOWERBIRD ♂
Chlamydera maculata
Eastern Australia 11–12 in.

GREEN CATBIRD ♂
Ailuroedus crassirostris
Northern Australia 14–15 in.

the forest. It covers this stage with fresh leaves, often of one particular kind. As the leaves wither, the bird replaces them with fresh ones. Well-used playgrounds are surrounded by a circle of the discarded debris. The male spends much of his time calling and singing from special perches above the plot, and is renowned as a ventriloquist and mimic.

Sanford's Golden-crested Bowerbird builds a similar but fancier circus ring on the floor of the mossy palm forests of New Guinea, some 8,000 feet above sea level. It mats its dancing ground with fern fronds and decorates the edges with piles of beetle wings, snail shells, and pieces of resin. Then it hangs a curtain of bamboo strands and wilted ferns from vines around its arena, among which it scatters pieces of bark, berries, and an occasional snail shell. The male maintains this stage throughout the breeding season, and daily redecorates it and poses and sings in and around it.

The maypole builders number five species. The Golden Bowerbird of northern Australia, only 9 inches long and one of the smallest of the family, builds one of the largest bowers, a roofed gazebo that in extreme cases may tower 9 feet in height. The other four maypole builders live in the New Guinea jungles at considerable altitudes. These birds plant mosses in their dancing grounds and are hence often referred to as the "gardeners." These four congeneric New Guinea species are the Crested, the Orange-crested, the Crestless, and the Golden-fronted gardeners. The Golden-fronted is one of the great ornithological rarities. The three known specimens reached Europe in 19th-century shipments of bird-of-paradise plumes. Though every expedition to New Guinea has searched for it, the bird has yet to be found in the wild.

The maypole builder starts his bower by piling sticks and twigs horizontally around the base of a small tree until they reach the desired height, usually 4 to 6 feet. He then builds a similar but smaller pyramid around the base of another sapling or shrub a few feet away and arches over the intervening space with vines and sticks so that it resembles a thatched roof. These structures are often used season after season, repaired and added to each year, and the largest ones may represent years of work. The birds decorate the walls and the ground under and around the bower with mosses, ferns, orchids and other flowers, and little orderly piles of bright berries and snail shells. As the flowers fade, the owner removes them and replaces them with fresh ones.

The nine species of avenue builders are considered the most highly specialized of the family. Though their bowers are not as massive as those of the maypole builders and are only partly roofed, if at all, their construction is more intricate. At least two species, the Satin and Regent bowerbirds of Australia, use tools—paint daubers—when decorating them.

The male avenue builder starts his bower by flooring a cleared space about 4 feet in diameter with a mat of well-trodden sticks and twigs several inches thick. In the center of this he erects two parallel walls of upright sticks firmly implanted and entwined together and sometimes arched over at the top. Dimensions vary somewhat between species. The Spotted Bowerbird of Australia makes a mat 6 to 8 inches thick with avenue walls 2 to 3 feet long and 16 inches high. The Regent Bowerbird builds walls only 8 inches long and 6 inches high. The walls are just far enough apart for the bird to walk through without brushing the sides with its wings. The birds decorate this playground with all sorts of strange objects such as pebbles, bleached bones, shells, leaves, and flowers.

The Regent and the Satin bowerbirds daub the inside walls of the bower with a bluish or greenish paint made of charcoal and other pigments mixed with saliva. The Regent takes a wad of green leaves in its beak and daubs the paint around with it; the Satin Bowerbird uses a wad of bark. The only other use of a "tool" by a bird that I can think of is that of the probing thorn of one of the Galapagos finches.

In five of the avenue builders, the Satin and Regent of Australia and the Black-faced Golden, the Yellow-throated Golden, and Baker's bowerbirds of New Guinea, the males are brightly colored, the females relatively drab and dull-colored. In the other four, all of the genus *Chlamydera,* both sexes are dull and nearly alike, their main coloring being a patch of elongated pink feathers on the nape, on the male alone in some, in both sexes in others. The *Chlamydera* group in both Australia and New Guinea live in open scrublands and often near grasslands. The largest member of the family, the 15-inch Great Gray Bowerbird of Australia, belongs to this genus.

The avenue builders are somewhat more gregarious than other bowerbirds, and outside the breeding season often travel about in small flocks of 4 to 6 birds. Their diet is principally fruits and berries, supplemented by insects of various sorts. The range of the Spotted Bowerbird in western Australia is apparently limited by the distribution of its principal food, a wild fig. Orchardists complain of their depredations, particularly of those of the Satin Bowerbird, which loves soft fruits. The call notes of this group are not particularly attractive, being guttural cries or sawlike wheezes, but like most bowerbirds they are good mimics and include the songs of other species in their repertoire when displaying.

BIRDS OF PARADISE

PASSERIFORMES   PARADISAEIDAE

In this family is the most ornate and colorful assemblage of birds in the world. In the male birds of paradise the development of special feathers for the attraction of the opposite sex reaches its peak, not only in varied bright colors but in weird and fanciful shapes. Yet the family is of lowly origin, for these 40 gorgeous birds evolved from some drab generalized, crowlike ancestors that became isolated in the Papuan region, probably fairly early in Tertiary time. Their closest living relatives are the bowerbirds, from which they differ in a few minor anatomical points such as relative length of toes, but primarily in their courtship behavior and in the ornamental plumages that are an integral part of their sex life.

The home of these splendid creatures is the forests of New Guinea and neighboring small islands. Four species occur in the mountain forests of northeastern Australia. Much of their habitat has only recently become accessible and is still relatively unexplored. Some forms are still known only by a specimen or two collected without data by native hunters. Only a score of trained ornithologists have had the good fortune to study these birds in their native haunts, and few have been able to spend more than several months in the field with them. Hence our knowledge of their behavior and life histories is rather sketchy. Much of what we know about their display has been learned by watching captive birds in zoos.

Yet modern knowledge of birds of paradise dates back 450 years. Primitive New Guinea tribes have used the plumes as ornaments from time immemorial, and Chinese voyagers and traders brought them to the Orient long before the 16th century. The first known in Europe were two native-made skins sent to the king of Spain by the ruler of Batjan, one of the Molucca Islands, and carried home aboard Magellan's circumnavigating *Victoria* in 1522. So unbelievably beautiful were these two birds that the Spaniards believed them visitors from paradise instead of from the Papuan jungles, and birds of paradise they have been ever since. The 16th- and 17th-century Portuguese traders knew them as "manucodiata," a corruption of the Malay phrase "manuq dewata," meaning "birds of the gods." This names survives in the five manucodes of New Guinea and the closely related Trumpeter Manucode of New Guinea and northeastern Australia, a shiny blackish bird that displays by erecting its long, shiny neck feathers in a wide ruff and produces its loud, deep notes in the long windpipe coiled about under the skin of its chest.

Most of the bird-of-paradise specimens that filtered back to Europe in the early days were native-made trade skins from which the savage taxidermists had removed the legs and feet. This gave rise to all sorts of fanciful tales—the birds were supposed never to alight, but to live on the wing and to fly continually toward the sun, and the female was supposed to lay her eggs in a hole in the male's back. The level-headed European naturalists of the 18th century must have known that these were just travelers' tales, and doubtless the great Linnaeus had his tongue in his cheek when, in the 1758 edition of his great "Systema Natura," he named the best-known one *Paradisaea apoda,* "the footless paradise bird." Linnaeus gave the locality for this species as "India" and that of the Little King Bird of Paradise, which he called *Paradisaea regia,* as the "East Indies." Both we now know came from the Aru Islands, the little group of satellite islands lying just southwest of the New Guinea mainland.

The actual source of the trade skins that were delighting

European naturalists was not discovered until 1824, when the French explorer-naturalist René Lesson collected specimens of the Trumpeter and Black manucodes in northwestern New Guinea. The first naturalist to study these birds extensively in their native haunts and publish sound observations of their habits was the English scientist Alfred Russell Wallace, who reached the Papuan region in the late 1850's. On the island of Batjan, where Magellan's ship had stopped 350 years earlier, Wallace discovered the fabulous Standardwinged Bird of Paradise which bears his name today—*Semioptera wallaceii*, a thrush-sized brownish bird with a shiny green gorget at its throat which it spreads in display, and two 6-inch white pennant feathers extending from the bend of each wing, which the bird erects in a V over its back when courting. Two Lesser Birds of Paradise that Wallace took back with him when he returned to England in 1862 were the first of the family to reach Europe alive.

By Wallace's time the demand for the fancy feathers for feminine adornment was extensive in the civilized world. By the 1890's an estimated 50,000 skins were being exported from New Guinea every year. Most of·them eventually reached Paris, then the center of the world's feather trade. Excited ornithologists searched for new and undescribed species in the wholesale markets and millinery shops.

Just how disastrous this wholesale exploitation was will never be known. The trade was prohibited by law in New Guinea in the 1920's, but by then many formerly common species had become rare. Public sentiment against the use of plumes has increased ever since, and it is now illegal to import wild-caught skins into the United States and most European countries. Some species are reported to have made a good comeback in the last several decades. However, the eventual deforestation of New Guinea for agriculture would certainly be calamitous for these magnificent birds, whose fascinating courtship habits we are just beginning to understand.

The birds most people picture as typical birds of paradise are the six jay-sized species of Linnaeus's genus *Paradisaea*.

These inhabitants of the wet lowland coastal jungles were common species of commerce. Their long, filmy flank plumes extend well beyond the tail when the bird is at rest and are raised over the back in a fountainlike spray in display. The shafts of the central tail feathers of the male are elongated thin wires or flattened narrow or twisted plumes. Their bodies are predominantly mauve, and they usually have patches of bright yellow on the back and head, and a brilliant greenish gorget at the throat. In the typical race of the Greater Bird of Paradise (Linnaeus's *apoda*), the trailing flank plumes are a bright yellow shading to mauve. These vary through orange to red in the Red Bird of Paradise, found only on the island of Waigeu off the northwest coast of New Guinea. Most of these birds display by crouching on a branch and waving their plumes above them. The Emperor of Germany Bird of Paradise starts his display right side up, and gradually tilts forward from the branch until he is hanging upside down with his plumes cascading around him. The rare and lovely Blue Bird of Paradise of the mountain forests of eastern New Guinea hangs upside down to start his display and then waves his gorgeous blue plumes in a lacy mist of blue spray around him.

Another species common among trade skins is the Twelve-wired Bird of Paradise found in the mangroves and sago swamp forests of coastal central and western New Guinea. Its six brilliant yellow plumes growing from each flank have long wiry tips bending sharply forward. When displaying to the drab brownish-barred female, the male Twelve-wire expands its bib of iridescent black-and-green throat feathers up around the bill and opens its bill to show its bright greenish-yellow mouth lining.

The 6-inch King Bird of Paradise is the smallest member of the family and one of the most brilliant; it is bright scarlet above and white below, and has bright blue legs and green plumes. Two of its tail feathers are elongated wires that end in curly metallic-green rackets. Conspicuous birds of the tree-tops, the male Kings apparently establish territories around the tall jungle trees where they display. This is the only species in the family known to nest in a hole in a tree.

Closely related to the King Bird of Paradise are two slightly larger species, the Magnificent and Wilson's. The Magnificent, found over much of the drier lowlands of New Guinea and up to about 5,000 feet in the mountains, makes a display ground for itself on the floor of the forest, stripping all vegetation from a stage some 15 feet in diameter and plucking the bark and the leaves from the saplings growing within it. The male dances up and down on these saplings, expanding his brilliant yellow crest in a fan like a cape and puffing out his glossy green chest feathers to reflect the light.

Because of the double cross of small, black velvety feathers on the bare blue skin of its crown, Wilson's Bird of Paradise is often called the "cross of Christ." Named *Paradisaea wilsoni* in 1850 by John Cassin, the Philadelphia naturalist, in honor of his friend Alexander Wilson, the same specimen had been named six months earlier by Charles Lucient Bonaparte, a nephew of Napoleon who spent some time in the United States and wrote extensively on American birds. Bonaparte called it *P. respublica* (the scientific name Wilson's Bird of Paradise holds today by right of priority) partly in honor of the French republic, partly to express his disapproval of some "republicans," for he commented, "Even though a paradisaean Republic does not exist, at least there is now a *Paradisaea respublica.*"

Many birds of paradise have been named for royalty. One of the earliest was Queen Victoria's Riflebird (*Ptiloris victoriae*) of Australia, named for his monarch by John Gould, the English artist-naturalist, in 1850. The Germans, who were active in New Guinea in the 1880's, named two outstanding species for their then emperor and empress (*P. guilielmi* and *P. augustaevictoria*). The Austrian Otto Finsch named the Blue Bird of Paradise *P. rudolphi,* in honor of Archduke Rudolph of Hapsburg, who died at Mayerling, and Princess Stephanie's Bird of Paradise (*Astrapia stephaniae*), one of the ribbon-tailed group, for Rudolph's consort.

Princess Stephanie's Bird of Paradise is another of the very few species that have bred in captivity, and is representative of a group of long-tailed birds of paradise sometimes called paradise magpies. All are inhabitants of the high mountain forests of New Guinea, where very few of them were caught for the feather trade. All have a shining metallic-black body, and many are endowed with brilliant, reflective neck ruffs and long, ornate tails. The male Ribbon-tailed Bird of Paradise has two white central tail feathers which stream 3 feet behind him in flight. This bird, discovered in 1939, has a total length of 42 inches and is the longest of all the passerine birds.

The largest-bodied birds of paradise are the crow-sized Sickle-bills of the New Guinea highlands, seldom found below 5,000 feet. In display the Sickle-bill raises epaulettes of long metal-tipped feathers growing along his flanks up over his head until they meet over his back; he opens and closes his long central tail feathers, and opens his bill to show the bright yellow lining.

Best known of the so-called flag birds is the Six-plumed Bird of Paradise, which has three wirelike plumes growing out of each side of the head, each tipped with a black racket.

1 LITTLE KING BIRD OF PARADISE ♂
Cicinnurus regius
New Guinea   7 in.

2 SUPERB BIRD OF PARADISE ♂
Lophorina superba
New Guinea   9½ in.

3 WILSON'S BIRD OF PARADISE ♂
Diphyllodes respublica
New Guinea   6½ in.

4 RED-PLUMED (COUNT RAGGI'S) ♂
BIRD OF PARADISE
Paradisaea apoda raggiana
New Guinea   18 in.

5 MAGNIFICENT RIFLE BIRD ♂
Craspedophora magnifica
New Guinea, northern Australia   13 in.

6 MAGNIFICENT ♂
BIRD OF PARADISE
Diphyllodes magnificus
New Guinea   8 in.

7 KING OF SAXONY BIRD OF PARADISE ♂
Pteridophora alberti
New Guinea   8 in.

8 PRINCE RUDOLPH'S ♂
BLUE BIRD OF PARADISE
Paradisaea rudolphi
New Guinea   13–14 in.

9 TWELVE-WIRED BIRD OF PARADISE ♂
Seleucides ignotus
New Guinea   13 in.

BIRDS OF PARADISE   **111**

Another is the King of Saxony, or Enameled, Bird of Paradise, a little 7-inch mite known only from the mountains of central New Guinea. Males have two long 18-inch plumes trailing backward from the head, each of which bears a series of 30 to 40 miniature flags along one side of the vane, a brilliantly enameled blue outside, brown inside. This bird, described in 1894 from a specimen found in a Paris market, is so unbelievable that conservative ornithologists of the time suspected that it was an artifact.

While their habits in the wild are still imperfectly known, a number of these fantastically plumed birds are polygamous, and as usual in such circumstances, all the nesting duties from building of the nest to feeding and rearing of the young are done by the duller, browner females. This, however, is not true throughout the family. The more primitive species, the manucodes and the wattled birds of paradise of the genera *Macgregoria* and *Paradigalla,* are often brilliantly colored, but have few or no plumes, and the male and female are similar in color. In the Black Manucode of New Guinea the males are monogamous, and while the female alone incubates through the 15- to 18-day incubation period, the male brings nest material for the female to work with, helps bring food to the young, and occasionally broods them.

The Magnificent Riflebird is found in both New Guinea and northeastern Australia. Its flank display plumes are soft and hairy and much shorter than those in many of the other groups. The bird has a brilliant throat of glossy purplish blue and poses with wings spread wide and its head thrown back to catch the rays of the sunlight on the throat. Riflebirds get their peculiar name from their call, a loud two-syllabled whistling note reminiscent of the whine of a bullet.

Related to the flag birds is the Lesser Superb Bird of Paradise, a small starling-sized species with two sets of plumes, a cap of more than 100 velvety black feathers behind the crown which can be elevated into a huge fan over the head, and a breast plate of metallic-green feathers which expands almost to meet the crown plumes. These plumes are so firmly muscled that the displaying birds can fly with them erect.

From the center of this feathery shield the bird opens its mouth to show the brilliant lining.

The soundest biological explanation so far proposed for the development of these fancy plumes and elaborate display patterns is the need for pronounced recognition marks between species to prevent hybridization between these promiscuous, polygamous birds. A score or more wild hybrids are known, more of them between than within genera. All of them occur between the most highly developed types, none among the more primitive forms. As most such hybrids are sterile and of no value in species survival, species recognition is highly important in these highly specialized forms that do not form permanent mating pairs. Some of the most gaudy patterns and weirdest displays have possibly evolved through the need to avoid such disadvantageous hybridizing.

TITMICE

PASSERIFORMES   PARIDAE

No more friendly group of birds exists than the 62 species of active tits, titmice, and chickadees. Bright-eyed, pert, curious, and unafraid they go about searching twigs and small branches for minute insects with little concern for humans. These wild birds can be tamed to take food from one's hand. Their lisping, reedy calls and their simple whistled songs are among the best known and best loved of bird sounds. Many species nest in bird boxes. The vernacular names "tit" and "titmouse" generally used for the group are of Anglo-Saxon origin, "tit" meaning a very small object, and "mouse" a corruption of "mase," an Anglo-Saxon name for several small birds.

The titmouse family is fairly well defined. Most of its members are very small birds less than 6 inches in length, the smallest measuring only 3 inches from tip of bill to tip of tail, the largest a bare 8 inches. All have soft, thick plumage, and the sexes are usually alike in color, mostly grays and browns, often boldly marked with black and white or blues and yellows, but never very bright, and never barred, streaked, or mottled. All have short, stout, pointed bills, the nostrils partly concealed by bristles, and small but strong legs and feet. Their rounded wings are of medium length and have 10 primary feathers, the outermost one only half the length of the second. Their tails vary from quite short to very long in a few species.

The relationships of titmice to other families are obscure, but the titmice show affinities in distribution, structure, and behavior to the crow-jay complex. Their present distribution strongly parallels that of the crow subfamily and suggests a similar Old World origin. Titmice have their greatest development in the Northern Hemisphere, are well represented in Africa south to the Cape of Good Hope, but are absent from the Australian region and from the oceanic islands. They have pushed southward in the New World only to the Guatemalan highlands.

Titmice are among the most adaptable and teachable of the very small birds—another similarity to the corvids. Laboratory tests have proved the titmice's ability to solve simple problems connected with obtaining food, a skill long known to cage-bird fanciers. The tricks tame titmice can be taught are amazing. The Varied Titmouse is the little bird that tells fortunes at shrine festivals and street fairs in Japan. At the command of its master it hops to its perch, takes a coin from your fingers, drops it into a cash box, opens the door of a miniature shrine, takes out your paper fortune, and tears off the wrapping so you receive it ready to read.

After the breeding season titmice roam through the woodlands in small family groups, and later gather in flocks of considerable size. These loose bands may include several species of titmice and sometimes nuthatches, creepers, kinglets, and woodpeckers, all moving steadily, working a limb here, a branch there, and then flitting on to the next tree.

While insects are their mainstay, titmice eat seeds, small fruits, and berries, especially in winter when insects are scarce. They come readily to feeders in suburban areas and are particularly fond of suet and sunflower seeds, which they hold between their feet and pound with their bills jay-fashion to open. The Crested Tit of northern Eurasia has the jaylike habit of storing food, caching spruce and pine seeds and insect pupae in bark crevices for later use.

Though titmice wander widely when not breeding and northern species may retreat hundreds of miles southward in severe winters, they are not strongly migratory. Their seasonal movements, as revealed by banding, are sporadic and irregular and seem conditioned by local availability of food.

Some 45 species, almost three-quarters of the family, are grouped in the single genus *Parus* of the subfamily Parinae. Typical of them is our familiar Black-capped Chickadee, whose clearly whistled "spring soon" or "sweet weather" cheers the New England countryside as the bleak days lengthen in late winter. In Europe and the British Isles lives the very similar Willow Tit, which gave Gilbert and Sullivan one of their happier inspirations—though "tit willow" is not part of the birds' vocabulary by any stretch of the imagination. The genus is represented by 11 species in North America and Mexico, and by 18 more in temperate Eurasia. The 5½-inch Great Tit, while the largest and commonest of Europe, is not the largest member of the family. This distinction goes to the 8-inch Sultan Tit, a resident of the hill forests from the eastern Himalayas through Burma, Siam, and Malaya to Sumatra. The Sultan Tit is a stocky black bird with golden-yellow underparts and a long yellow crest.

A number of titmice of the genus *Parus* have distinctive head crests which stand up all the time. The Crested Tit of northern Eurasia is one example, the Tufted Titmouse of the southeastern United States another. The 6½-inch Tufted Titmouse, a mouse-colored bird with rusty flanks and all the friendly characteristics of its chickadee relatives, is the largest member of the family in North America.

Practically all the parine titmice are cavity nesters. A few

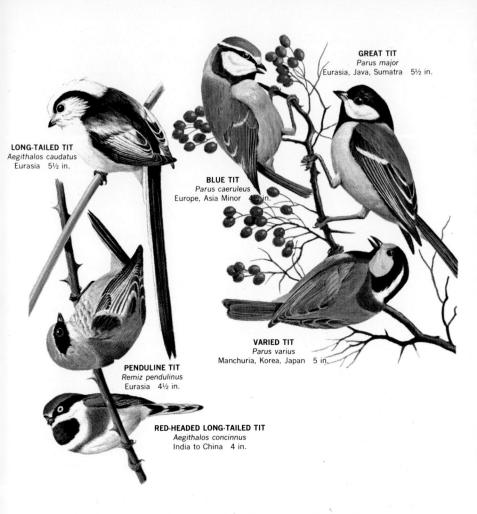

GREAT TIT
Parus major
Eurasia, Java, Sumatra   5½ in.

LONG-TAILED TIT
Aegithalos caudatus
Eurasia   5½ in.

BLUE TIT
Parus caeruleus
Europe, Asia Minor   4½ in.

VARIED TIT
Parus varius
Manchuria, Korea, Japan   5 in.

PENDULINE TIT
Remiz pendulinus
Eurasia   4½ in.

RED-HEADED LONG-TAILED TIT
Aegithalos concinnus
India to China   4 in.

chip their own holes out of half-rotten stubs or fenceposts; others use available natural cavities in trees or those deserted by woodpeckers. Still others nest in nooks and crannies in rocky cliffs. Nesting behavior is similar throughout the subfamily. The female usually builds the nest, and the male sometimes assists by bringing material to her. In the Black-capped Chickadee both sexes work at hewing out the nesting cavity and lining it with grasses, feathers, and hair; in the Crested Tit the female does all the nest building. Incubation is always by the female alone, but the male feeds her while she is incubating. Both sexes feed the young.

116   TITMICE

The parine titmice are normally single-brooded, but they lay large clutches, rarely as few as 5 to 6 eggs, more frequently 7 to 11, and as many as 15 have been recorded. In a few species the eggs are pure white; in most they are speckled with reddish brown. Large families are needed to offset the high natural mortality in the titmice, which averages 70 per cent in the adults and is even higher in the young during their first year. With almost three-fourths of the population dying each year, less than one per cent of the wild birds live more than 4 years. The longevity record for wild titmice is 8 years, attained by a Black-capped Chickadee banded on Cape Cod.

The subfamily Aegithalinae contains a dozen tiny titmice with long tails. Typical of this group is the Long-tailed Tit of Eurasia, a tame and confiding little mite that can be approached within a few feet. One of the smallest is the Pygmy Tit of Java, barely 3 inches long, and most of it tail. Close relatives are the sociable little Bush Tits of our Western states and the Mexican highlands, dull gray and brown little birds with the roving habits typical of the family.

The Long-Tailed Tits make beautiful bag nests with a side entrance, woven of mosses, lichens, and spider webs and lined with feathers. Pairs spend 2 to 3 weeks together building it in a bush or tree. As in the chickadee group, the male feeds the female on the nest. So small is the nest's cramped interior that the sitting bird has to curl her tail to fit in. The Long-tailed Tit lays from 7 to 12 eggs, white with small red spots. Incubation takes 12 to 13 days.

A third subfamily, Remizinae, consists of the eight species commonly known as the Penduline Tits because of the long hanging bag nests most of them make. The side entrances of their nests are usually protected by short tunnels, which some African species are reported to bite shut behind them. The Penduline Tit of Eurasia, with its distinctive black facial mask, is one of the better-known species. The only American member of this subfamily is the Verdin, a tiny olive-gray bird that lives in western chaparral country. The Verdin builds a large globular nest of thorny twigs that is so impregnable the bird makes no attempt to conceal it, but places it conspicuously near the end of a branch of a shrub or low tree.

The Penduline Tits lay smaller clutches than the other titmice, usually 4 to 5 eggs, but most of them are double-brooded. The males seem to do most of the nest building, and the females all the incubating and rearing of the young. The males often make several nests, and the female chooses one to lay in. The others are used for roosting at night. Roosting within their nesting cavities is a common habit among all titmice.

CREEPERS

PASSERIFORMES   CERTHIIDAE

There is no mistaking these slender, little brown birds that creep unobtrusively up and around tree trunks. Streaked and spotted above and whitish below, they are almost invisible against the bark. They have thin, pointed, down-curved bills for probing into bark crevices, and long, stiff tail feathers pointed at the end. Creepers use their tails as props for climbing, as do woodpeckers, and they molt their tail feathers in the same way, from the outermost pair inward in succession. They are the only passerines in which the central pair of tail feathers remain in place until all the others are replaced.

These "true" creepers number five species, all placed in the single genus *Certhia*, which is restricted to the Northern Hemisphere. The principal species is called the Brown Creeper in North America, the Tree Creeper in Europe. This wide-ranging little bird, found throughout the forested portions of North America and Eurasia, breaks into about a dozen geographical races on each continent. The four other species are all very similar birds found along the southern

BROWN CREEPER
Certhia familiaris
Forested North America and Eurasia   5 in.

periphery of the family's range in the Old World. In the New World the Brown Creeper has reached southward to the mountains of Nicaragua, but its ecological niche is filled from Central America southward by the strikingly similar woodcreepers.

Creepers are generally solitary birds that stay by themselves and go their own way. They live almost entirely on bark insects, and their eggs and larvae. Unlike the nuthatches, which search trees up, down, and sideways, head down as well as head up, the Brown Creeper usually works steadily up the tree trunk in a spiral, working systematically to the top and then fluttering down to the base of the next tree to repeat the maneuver. To rework a rewarding section of bark, it drops down backwards a few feet, tail first, with a fluttering of wings, and climbs back up again. It explores the bottoms and sides of horizontal branches as well as their tops, and has no trouble clinging to the underside of a limb like a fly on the ceiling.

The call notes of the Brown Creeper are high-pitched, sibilant squeaks, weak and hard to hear, though the bird utters them frequently while feeding and occasionally in flight. The species also has an attractive little musical song in the spring. Clear, sweet, polysyllabic, and pitched very high in the upper registers of human hearing, its low intensity is in keeping with the singer's small size and unprepossessing manner.

The Brown Creeper builds a hammock-shaped, elongated cup nest, usually wedged against the trunk of a dead tree behind a piece of loose bark. Cunningly woven of thin strips of bark, mosses, and fine grass on a base of slender twigs, it is lined with soft bark, spider webs, and feathers. Both sexes work at nest building. In the American races, only the females incubate, though the male is believed to assist in some of the European forms. The eggs number 6 to 7, occasionally as many as 9, and are white with a fine peppering of small reddish-brown dots. The incubation period is from 13 to 15 days, and the young spend another two weeks in the nest, where both parents feed them until they are able to climb out and hitch over the surface of the bark to find food for themselves.

NUTHATCHES
AND ALLIES

PASSERIFORMES   SITTIDAE

The acrobatic nuthatches are the only tree-trunk foragers that habitually hunt downward. Perhaps from their head-down viewpoint they find tidbits the competing creepers and small woodpeckers overlook. Nuthatches live largely on the small insects and spiders they ferret out of crannies in the bark, but also eat some seeds and nuts. Several Old World species hew acorns and hazelnuts open by wedging them in crevices and hacking them with the bill, swinging their tiny bodies to drive home each blow. The name comes from this habit, rarely observed in the American nuthatches, and is a corruption of "nuthack." It has nothing to do with incubating.

The name nuthatch is most properly applied to the 15 species of the genus *Sitta* and the subfamily Sittinae found throughout the forested regions of the Northern Hemisphere. These are stocky, short-necked little birds dressed in plain solid colors, usually gray to blue above and white below. Many have the underparts tinged with reddish brown, and the top of the head is often black or brown. Their bills are thin, straight, and sharp-pointed, and their legs short but stout. Their long, strong toes are tipped with sharp claws that give them sure footing on vertical bark surfaces. Unlike the woodpeckers and the true creepers, nuthatches do not use their tail in climbing but rely entirely on their feet to hold them in place. Instead of being stiff and spiny, their tails are soft, short, and squared or rounded.

Like their nearest relatives, the titmice, the nuthatches are best developed in the Old World, where they doubtless had their origin. Only four species occur in the New World, and the family is unknown south of central Mexico. Largest of the North American species is the White-breasted Nuthatch, common in the deciduous woodlands of the United States and a frequent visitor to city parks and suburbs. The Red-breasted Nuthatch prefers coniferous forests and breeds from the Canadian spruce zones southward through the Appalachians and the Rockies to northern Mexico. The Pygmy Nuthatch is a western species; the Brown-headed is a resident of the southeastern U. S. lowlands.

Widest ranging of the Old World species is the common Eurasian Nuthatch, which strongly resembles our Red-breasted. It breeds across the continent, usually in deciduous woodlands, from Great Britain and Spain to Kamchatka,

Japan, and China. One of the most striking is the blue-backed Velvet-fronted Nuthatch, found in southeastern Asian forests from India to the Philippines. Similar to the Velvet-fronted, but with the head and abdomen velvety black, is the southernmost of the *Sittas,* the Azure Nuthatch of the mountain forests of Malaya, Java, and Sumatra.

Two *Sittas* have left the woodlands to live among the bare rocks of highland cliffs, canyons, and gorges. These are the rock nuthatches of southeastern Europe and the Himalayas. Light-gray birds with brown washings on their white underparts, they hop and climb around the rock faces with the same agility and mannerisms that their tree-trunk-loving relatives display.

Nuthatches are droll, earnest little birds, quite tame and fearless and always busily searching for food. Rather solitary and usually met singly or in pairs, they come to feeding stations readily and can be induced, with patience, to take food from the fingers. Though they roam widely when not breeding, nuthatches are not strongly migratory, and most are resident where they occur. Northern forms move slightly southward in search of food during the winter, and mountain species seek lower levels during cold weather. One or two can often be found with the loose flocks of titmice, kinglets, and small woodpeckers that rove the temperate woodlands in winter.

Most nuthatches have distinctive metallic and penetrating call notes, easy to recognize. The American White- and Red-breasted nuthatches utter unmistakable nasal "yank-yanks" as they clamber about. Many of them also have unprepossessing spring songs, varied, bubbling, and quite musical, but hard to hear; these are delivered quietly as if the bird were singing under its breath.

All the *Sittas* are cavity nesters, and all but the rock nuthatches use natural holes in trees. Both sexes work at lining the cavity with grasses, mosses, and very often with animal hair. The Old World species have the peculiar habit of reducing the size of the entrance to their nest cavity by

WALL CREEPER
Tichodroma muraria
Mountains of central Eurasia   6½ in.

PIGMY NUTHATCH
Sitta pygmaea
Western North America
4¼ in.

WHITE-BREASTED NUTHATCH
Sitta carolinensis
Southern Canada to Mexico   5½ in.

RED-BREASTED NUTHATCH
Sitta canadensis
Northern North America   4½ in.

VELVET-FRONTED NUTHATCH
Sitta frontalis
Southeastern Asia   5 in.

plastering it with mud, presumably for added safety. This technique is most pronounced in the rock nuthatches, which build cone-shaped nests entirely of mud in cavities between the rocks, or projecting 6 or 8 inches from a rock face. Strangely, none of the New World nuthatches does this, though the Red-breasted Nuthatch smears the edges of its nesting hole with pine pitch.

The sittine nuthatches lay white eggs speckled with red-brown. The clutch may vary from 4 to 10, and incubation is apparently by the female alone. The male feeds her on the nest throughout the 12- to 14-day incubation period, and he always helps feed the young until they fledge. Nuthatches are generally multibrooded.

Classified here with the nuthatches are 14 Old World birds of uncertain systematic position, some formerly placed with the creepers. Most have slender, down-curved bills, and are commonly called "creepers," but as they lack the creepers' stiff, spring-tails, they are now included tentatively as subfamilies of the nuthatches. Some perhaps deserve separate family rank such as the six Australian species of streaked brownish birds 5 to 6 inches long called tree-creepers (*Climacteris*) that feed on the ground as well as on tree trunks, and are hole nesters like most nuthatches. Possibly allied to them are two aberrant Philippine creepers (*Rhabdornis*), the Striped-headed and the Plain-headed, both also hole nesters. These birds not only take insects from bark crevices, but have brush-tipped tongues and feed among flowers.

Largest of the nuthatches and placed in a subfamily by itself is the singular Wallcreeper with its startling red wing coverts. Wallcreepers inhabit rocky cliffs in the mountains of southern Europe and eastward through the Himalayas. Wallcreepers climb over the sheer rock walls hunting insects. They assist their progress up the vertical rock faces with short wing flicks that flash their red and white markings, darting out occasionally to snatch a passing insect on the wing. Their flight is peculiarly halting and butterfly-like; in fact, mountaineers call them "butterfly birds."

The Wallcreeper builds a nest of grasses and moss lined with hair and a stray feather or two, deep in an inaccessible crevice. The male may bring nest material and he helps feed the young, but the female builds the nest and does all the incubating. In winter Wallcreepers retreat to lower altitudes, where they sometimes have trouble finding the precipitous surroundings they prefer, and are seen scaling the walls of tall buildings.

Placed in another subfamily are the two Spotted Creepers (*Salpornis*) of Africa and India, and the three small Sitellas or tree runners (*Neositta*) of Australia and New Guinea. These birds act and look like true creepers, except for their soft tails, but they build open cup nests in forked branches. One of the rarest and least-known members of the family is the Red-fronted Creeper (*Daphoenositta*) of New Guinea.

SPOTTED CREEPER
Salpornis spilonotus
Tropical Africa   5 in.

STRIPE-HEADED CREEPER
Rhabdornis mystacalis
Philippines   6 in.

RED-BROWED TREECREEPER
Climacteris erythrops
Eastern Australia   5½ in.

125

BABBLERS AND ALLIES

PASSERIFORMES   TIMALIIDAE

This large assemblage of some 287 Old World forest birds is one of the most diverse of all passerine families. Its members range from tiny birds such as titmice or wrens to some the size of small crows. Some look and act like tits, others like woodland rails or pittas, still others like thrashers, thrushes, or crows. Many are dull-colored and undistinctive; others are brightly hued and strongly patterned. Some build open cup-shaped nests, others build domed structures with side entrances, but all nest on or fairly near the ground. Most of them are noisy birds (hence the name babblers) of woodlands or brushlands that travel through the undergrowth in small flocks and keep up a more or less continual chatter of chirps and churrs. All are insect eaters; a few add small fruits and seeds to their normal diet of small animal life.

Anatomically the family is poorly defined and loosely delimited, but all its members have soft, fluffy plumage and comparatively large, strong legs and feet. All are rather weak fliers with short rounded wings that curve to fit closely to the body. All have wings with 10 primary feathers, the first 3 unequal in length and shorter than the longest one. Normally the 12-feathered tail is fairly broad and square or rounded, though it is long and pointed in a few species. The bills vary from short and stout to slender and down-curved, but are always shorter than the tarsus. The culmen is more or less ridged and curved at the tip, and sometimes ends in a shrikelike hook. The upper mandible usually has a slight notch near its tip.

The babbler family's distribution is essentially the wooded portions of Old World central and southern land masses. The greatest number of them are found in the oriental region, and the family is well represented in Australia and in Africa.

Its northernmost members are the little crowtits that range from southwestern Europe eastward across temperate Asia to Korea. The Wrentit of our West Coast scrublands, sometimes put in a family by itself, is the only member of the family in the New World. A number of genera have disjointed ranges in Africa and Asia.

If the family as now constituted is a natural assemblage (which is open to question), its diversity and the spotty, scattered distribution of many of its components suggest it is of ancient lineage. Its members show similarities to so many other passerine families that the affinities of the group as a whole cannot be determined. They probably represent early offshoots from some primitive Old World insect-eating ancestor or ancestors that also gave rise to the Old World bulbuls, warblers, thrushes, and flycatchers. Only within the last few decades has some order been made out of the welter of different species assigned to the family Timaliidae. They are now sorted into seven fairly distinctive subfamilies, some of which are so divergent in appearance, habits, and distribution that many students accord them full family rank.

The ground-babbler subfamily (Cinclosomatinae) contains 17 terrestrial species restricted to the Australo-Papuan region, though one species, the Malay Rail-babbler, extends northward into Malaya. The ground babblers are varicolored birds with very soft, fluffy plumage, long legs, rather small feet, and thin necks. They live on the forest floor, often near fallen timber, and scurry through the underbrush much like rails or pittas.

Typical of the group is the Cinnamon Quail-thrush of Australia. These birds go about in pairs or small parties and, though fairly noisy, keep well hidden in the undergrowth. They fly with an audible whirring of wings, but only when closely pressed, and then for a very short distance. They drop quickly into cover, run off through the underbrush, and are difficult to flush a second time. The quail-thrushes build open cup-shaped nests on the ground, in which they lay 2 to 3 heavily spotted eggs.

Other interesting Australian members of this group are the logrunners, or spinetails (*Orthonyx*), which are similarly retiring birds of the underbrush, but have more pleasant voices. They scratch in the ground debris for their food, mainly insects, slugs, and snails, and reportedly use their tails as well as their feet for the purpose, raking the ground sideways with the spiny tips of their short tail feathers, a most unusual habit known in no other bird. The spinetails build a domed nest of sticks and moss with a side entrance on or near the ground. They lay two pure-white eggs which take about 3 weeks to hatch.

The jungle-babbler subfamily (Pellorneinae) contains 32 species of small, secretive, brownish birds from 6 to 8 inches in length found from the Philippines through the oriental region, where they are most plentiful, and in Africa. Jungle-babblers have rather slender bills, often strongly hooked at the tip, and look much like some of the Old World warblers. They inhabit low forest thickets where their somber plumage and skulking habits make them extremely hard to observe. Representative of the group is the Striped Jungle-babbler, which ranges from India to Indochina in the low brush-woods and bamboo jungles from sea level up to perhaps 4,000 feet. Fairly common throughout its range, the Striped Jungle-babbler is more often heard than seen. Its loud mellow calls and whistled chatterings are familiar sounds in the Burmese jungles. Jungle-babblers travel about in small flocks and feed largely on insects and small mollusks. They build large globular nests of leaves and moss on or close to the ground, often in the shelter of a low shrub, and lay 2 to 4 heavily spotted eggs.

The third subfamily, the Pomatorhininae, is commonly known as the scimitar-babblers and wren-babblers. The group's 36 species range throughout the Orient from India to eastern China and south through the East Indies into Australia. All are somberly streaked and mottled in browns. The scimitar-babblers are thrush-sized birds 7 to 11 inches long, with long tails and long down-curved bills, that superficially resemble the thrashers of the New World. Wren-babblers are smaller birds 3½ to 6 inches long, wrenlike in appearance as their name implies. The two extremes are connected by many intermediate forms.

Shy, retiring denizens of the forest understory, the scimitar-babblers and wren-babblers feed on or near the ground and are known for their habit of digging into the earth with their bills. Many of them have pleasant songs. All build domed nests of rather loose, fragile construction. Their eggs vary greatly, some being pure white, others heavily spotted with dark browns. The Gray-crowned Scimitar-babbler of eastern Australia has the typical babbler trait of traipsing through the forest undergrowth in small noisy bands. Its gregariousness and its distinctive calls have earned it such local names as apostle bird, happy family, chatterer, cackler, and yahoo.

The 38 species classified as tit-babblers (Timaliinae) include some of the more brightly colored members of the family. Their fluffy plumage often exhibits contrasting patterns of white and black, browns, grays, and yellows. They have short titmouse-like bills and large, strong legs and feet. They range from the Philippines westward through the oriental region to India, and four species of one genus, *Neomixis,* are marooned in Madagascar. While they have the general flocking habits of the family, the tit-babblers are not noisy, few have a real song, and all tend to be less terrestrial. Some live entirely in trees, a few live in everegreen forests in the highlands, and a number are addicted to open scrub country and grasslands. Most of them make bell-like domed nests, but a few build deep cups. The striking Red-capped Babbler, which ranges from India to the Philippines and southward to Java, is fairly typical of the subfamily. This species is partial to canebrakes and grassy plains.

The largest, most widespread, and perhaps most typical group of babblers consists of the 140-odd laughing thrushes of the subfamily Turdoidinae. The laughing thrushes are found in Africa, throughout India and the oriental region,

RED-CAPPED BABBLER
Timalia pileata
Himalayas to Indochina and Java   7 in.

**STRIPED
JUNGLE BABBLER**
Pellorneum ruficeps
India to Indochina   6½ in.

PEKIN ROBIN
Leiothrix lutea
Himalayas and
southern China   6 in.

WHITE-CRESTED LAUGHING THRUSH
Garrulax leucolophus
Himalayas to Indochina   12 in.

SILVER-EARED MESIA
Leiothrix argentauris
Himalayas to Indochina   7 in.

GRAY-CROWNED SCIMITAR-BABBLER
Pomatostomus temporalis
Eastern Australia   10 in.

CINNAMON QUAIL-THRUSH
Cinclosoma cinnamomeum
Interior of Australia   9 in.

**RED-WINGED (BLACK-CROWNE
SHRIKE-BABBLER**
Pteruthius erythropterus
Himalayas to Indochina   6½

and south into the East Indies. They are a highly variable group ranging from about 4 to 12 inches in length. Some are dull-colored; others show the gayest hues of any member of the family, with bright yellows, reds, and greens showing in bold patterns. The laughing-thrush complex is best developed in the hill forests from India through southern China and Malaya where some of the brightest and most colorful species occur. Here live the Red-winged Shrike-babbler and the Red-billed Leiothrix, which, though a bird of the Himalayan foothills, is commonly known as the Pekin Robin. Its bright colors and attractive song have made it a popular cage bird in India.

Laughing thrushes are noisy birds with wide vocal ranges, given to chattering choruses that have the quality of distant human laughter. Essentially arboreal forest dwellers, many of them feed on the ground, and some are common garden residents in India and the Orient. Primarily insectivorous,

**BALD CROW
(BARE-HEADED ROCK FOWL)**
Picathartes gymnocephalus
Tropical West Africa   14 in.

VINOUS-THROATED CROWTIT
Paradoxornis webbiana
Manchuria and Ussuria to Burma   4½ in.

many of them eat seeds and small fruit as well. Most build cup nests in trees or bushes; a few have domed nests on or near the ground.

The sixth subfamily of this widely varying family, the Paradoxornithinae, contains the northern outliers of the group, the 20 species of crowtits or parrotbills of central and eastern Asia. Once classified as titmice, crowtits have short, heavy bills, laterally compressed like a parrot's—hence the name parrotbill often used for the group. Crowtits are active little birds that wander through grasslands, brushlands, hedgerows, and thickets in flocks of 50 or more, hunting seeds, berries, and small insects. They work over reed stems and thicket twigs at gravity-defying angles while keeping up a twittering chattering to one another. They act so much like the non-tippable "daruma" dolls set on a round base that the Japanese name "daruma tit" for the Vinous-throated Crowtit of China and Korea is most apt.

Another member of this subfamily formerly classified with the titmice is the Bearded Tit, so called for the male's black mustache stripes. A resident of reedy marshes from southern Europe to Manchuria, the Bearded Tit behaves much like the parrotbills, and is similarly gregarious, acrobatic, and garrulous. All these titlike babblers build deep cup nests of grasses and reeds lined with plant fibers, hair, and a feather or two. In the Bearded Tit both sexes build the nest and the male adds the lining. Their clutches are large for timaliids, 5 to 7 white eggs, heavily blotched with brown. Both sexes incubate for a period of 12 to 13 days; the fledging period is 9 to 12 days, and the species is multi-brooded.

Now thought a possible offshoot from the crowtits is the unique Wrentit, isolated in the scrublands west of the Rocky Mountains from Oregon south to Baja California. If it is a crowtit, it is the only member of the family to have reached the New World. This fluffy little gray-brown bird shows no close affinities to any of the American passerines, and the American Check-list places it in a family by itself—the Chamaeidae. Wrentits are weak fliers and move through the thickets by hopping from twig to twig. Though the immature birds wander widely in the fall and winter, adults are very sedentary. Wrentits appear to mate for life, and each pair to remain all year within its acre or two of territory. Banding has shown these little 6-inch mites may live 10 years, a long life span indeed for so small a bird.

Recently placed with the babblers as a seventh subfamily, the Picathartinae, are two strange birds of West Africa known as Bareheaded Rock Fowl. The two species differ largely in the color of their heads, the bare skin being blue and red in the Cameroon species, bright yellow in the bird of Sierra Leone. Both species live on the ground in wet highlands where tall forest trees shelter large moss-covered boulders. Few Europeans have ever had the opportunity to study the Rock Fowl in their native haunts, and the African natives attribute magical powers to them. They are reported to be somewhat gregarious, to fly little, to move gracefully on the ground, and to be curious enough to investigate anything unusual in the vicinity. Rather quiet birds, Rock Fowl have low croaking calls, and feed on insects, small frogs, crustaceans, and snails. They nest in colonies and build mud nests lined with vegetable fibers and a few feathers; the nests are plastered to cliff faces 5 to 15 feet above the ground, often sheltered from rain by a rocky overhang. They lay two creamy-white eggs heavily mottled with brown.

BULBULS

PASSERIFORMES   PYCNONOTIDAE

Bulbuls are among the better known and more familiar of the local songbirds throughout the family's extensive range in southern Asia and Africa. Many have adapted themselves to cultivated lands and have become common residents around villages, in suburban gardens and orchards, and even in city parks. Of moderate size and rather plainly garbed, most bulbuls are not striking in appearance, but they generally make themselves conspicuous by their actions. They are gregarious, industrious and inquisitive, and fairly bold and noisy. Their most winning attributes are their cheerful friendliness and their constant musical chattering. Many have pleasant songs.

The bulbul family is large, with 119 species, and fairly well defined. An outstanding characteristic, though sometimes partly concealed, is a patch of hairlike, vaneless feathers on the nape. Bulbuls range in length from 6 to 11 inches. Their necks and wings are short, their tails medium to long and sometimes slightly forked. Bills are somewhat slender, slightly down-curved, and hooked and notched in some species. Most bulbuls are somberly clad in grays, browns, dull greens, or black, often relieved by patches of yellow or red and white about the head and undertail coverts. A number of species are crested. The sexes are similarly colored but males are sometimes slightly larger.

The bulbuls are a rather primitive group of Old World oscines, believed most closely allied to the babblers, from which they differ mainly in having shorter legs and feet and well-developed rictal bristles. Their dull colors and their soft, fluffy plumage, especially their thick patch of long rump feathers, suggest possible affinities to the cuckoo-shrikes. Like both the babblers and cuckoo-shrikes, the bulbuls are essentially forest inhabitants, though a number live in scrub country and in open grasslands if shrubby cover is available. They have adapted well to man-made changes in their natural environment. Their altitudinal range extends from sea level up to 10,000 feet in the Himalayas.

The bulbul family is best developed in Africa and Madagascar, where all but one of its 14 genera occur. Nine of the African genera are either monotypic or have only two or three species. Four of the larger genera have representatives ranging widely from Africa across southern Asia to Japan, the Philippines, and the Moluccas. The largest and most familiar

RED-WHISKERED BULBUL
Pycnonotus jocosus
India to China, Indochina, Java, Sumatra   8 in.

group consists of the 47 species in the nominate genus *Pycnonotus*, of which the Red-whiskered Bulbul is typical.

The Red-whiskered Bulbul, a common Asiatic species, is found from India to China and south through Malaysia. Always lively and on the go, this bird prefers human settlements to the heavy jungles. Its short, bright call notes vie with the chatterings of sparrows and starlings around rural oriental villages. A cheerful and conspicuous resident of orchards and gardens, it scurries through the trees looking for ripening fruit or over the grass in search of insects, its tail cocked at a jaunty angle, and bathes in puddles left by a passing shower. It tames easily and is a popular oriental cage bird. Introduced to New South Wales some years ago, the Red-whiskered Bulbul has become well established in suburban Sydney and Melbourne. It is something of a nuisance to fruit growers, often damaging crops enough to become a problem.

While bulbuls eat some insects and other animal food, their mainstay is berries and fruit. They are gross and intemperate feeders, and occasionally get tipsy on overripe fermenting fruit, a frailty they share with a number of other fruit-eating birds.

Most bulbuls are gregarious and when not nesting go about in small flocks searching for food and taking an alert interest in everything that goes on. They are not strongly territorial and do not establish property rights, but they are keen to potential danger and spread the alarm when they spot a prowling cat or snake. If an owl appears all bulbuls in the vicinity gather to mob and harass it until it moves on. They will also attack nest-robbing crows and magpies.

The short-winged bulbuls are not strong fliers and tend to be resident wherever they occur. Highland species move to lower levels in winter, and some of the lowland tropical species shift their feeding grounds seasonally, following the ripening fruit. The only truly migratory members of the family are the northern populations of the Brown-eared Bulbul of eastern Asia and Japan.

The Brown-eared Bulbul is representative of some 20 species of the genus *Hypsipetes,* found widely from eastern Asia and the Philippines westward to India and southward on islands in the Indian Ocean to Madagascar. Their habits are those of the rest of the family, but their voices are more raucous. The Japanese Brown-eared Bulbuls all move southward in winter, traveling by day, and are often seen in large flocks flying across the straits from one island to another. The bulbul population of Hokkaido, the northernmost of the Japanese islands, crosses the Japan Sea and winters in Korea and eastern China.

So far as known all bulbuls build open cup nests woven of grasses and fibers in the branches of a shrub or tree. The nesting habits of the Brown-eared Bulbul are typical of the family. It makes a deep cup of leaves, grasses, moss, and bark, often lined with pine needles, rootlets, and the slender leaves of bamboo, from 5 to 15 feet up in a tree or thicket. The nest is always cleverly concealed and hard to find. In it the female lays a single clutch of 3 to 5 (usually 4) eggs, pinkish gray marked with red, black, and purplish spots. Incubation is mainly, if not entirely, by the female. The male feeds her on the nest and helps brood and feed the nestlings. The young are fed at first on insects, later on small berries. The tropical bulbuls usually have smaller clutches, 2 to 3 eggs, and pairs are multibrooded.

African representatives of the genus *Pycnonotus* include the Black-capped, White-eared, and White-vented bulbuls. Like the Red-whiskered Bulbul, all are tame, cheery, conspicuous inhabitants of forest edges, gardens, and villages.

YELLOW-STREAKED GREENBUL
Phyllastrephus flavostriatus
Tropical Africa   8 in.

More strictly forest dwellers are the shyer and less well known leaf-loves and bristle-bills. The best known of these African forest bulbuls are the 22 members of the genus *Phyllastrephus,* commonly called greenbuls or brownbuls. These birds all have greenish to brownish backs and yellowish underparts, and many are so alike they are hard to tell apart in the field. The females in this genus are noticeably smaller than the males and have shorter bills. The greenbuls eat more insects than they do fruit, and many are fine singers. They share the common bulbul traits of being active, curious, and rather tame, but have a characteristic habit of flicking their tail and wings—often one wing at a time.

How the odd-sounding name bulbul became attached to these birds is uncertain. The word is an ancient Arabic and Persian term for a small bird, and was probably imitative in origin. It occurs frequently in the writings of the medieval poets Omar Khayyam and Hafiz. English versions of these works usually translate it as "nightingale," and are probably correct in so doing, for several of the true nightingales (small thrushes of the genus *Luscinia*) are fairly common songsters in Turkestan, Iran, and Iraq. Later Muslim poets in India and Pakistan, where no true nightingales occur, are believed to have transferred the Persian word to the pycnonotids, several of which, notably the White-cheeked and the Red-whiskered bulbuls, are cheerful, noisy, familiar inhabitants of Indian gardens and open country.

LEAFBIRDS AND ALLIES

PASSERIFORMES   IRENIDAE

Closely related to the bulbuls and sometimes classified with them are 14 species of more brilliantly colored forest birds of southeastern Asia. Divided among three distinct genera, they are known respectively as leafbirds, ioras, and fairy bluebirds. They share several characteristics with the bulbuls, including the long, fluffy rump feathers and the hairlike feathers on the nape. But unlike the bulbuls, the males are always more brightly colored than the drab females.

Leafbirds are medium-sized (7 to 8 inches) denizens of the forest crown. The eight species are all predominantly bright green, variously marked with blue, orange, yellow, and black. Typical is the Golden-fronted Leafbird, a common species from northern India to Burma and Sumatra. When not nesting leafbirds travel through the woodland canopy in small noisy bands. Despite their bright colors they are difficult to see in the treetops. They eat some seeds and insects, but fruit and nectar are their mainstay. They often gather with other species to feast in the tops of fruiting or flowering trees. They are especially fond of the nectar and the berries of the oriental mistletoes (*Loranthus*), and are a factor in both pollinating and spreading these common tree parasites.

All leafbirds are fine singers and accomplished mimics that copy the songs and calls of other species. Their rich and varied singing, bright colors, and adaptability to confinement make them popular cage birds that find a ready market in the Orient. They are so aggressive and pugnacious, however, that they are not suitable for mixed aviaries.

Leafbirds build small, shallow cup-shaped nests of fine roots and grasses, unlined but coated on the outside with soft fibers, on a bough or fork 20 feet or so above the ground. When nesting they are exceedingly alert and watchful; but they are so noisy and excitable that when danger threatens they usually betray the location of their nests by their obviously anxious behavior.

The four ioras are smaller birds, 5 to 6 inches long, with yellow or olive-green and black their predominant colors. Like the rest of the family, ioras are arboreal birds, but they feed almost entirely on insects, are not gregarious, and usually frequent the forest borders and edges of clearings. The Common Iora, a common resident of village gardens, is plentiful from India through Malaya.

1 GOLDEN-FRONTED LEAFBIRD ♂
Chloropsis aurifrons
India to Annam and Sumatra 8 in.

2 FAIRY BLUEBIRD ♂
Irena puella
India to Indochina and East Indies 10 in.

3 COMMON IORA
Aegithina tiphia
India to Indochina 6 in.

The courtship of the Common Iora includes a striking song flight. Flying up into the air, the male fluffs his feathers, especially those of the rump, until he is as round as a ball. Then he spirals slowly to his perch whistling a thin piping note like that of a cricket or a tree frog. He continues the display on his perch, posturing with feathers still fluffed and wings drooping, spreading and flicking his tail and whistling steadily. Ioras build neat, frail cup nests of grasses bound together with spider webs, usually in a fork 5 to 30 feet above the ground. They lay 2 to 4 creamy-white eggs streaked with gray or brown.

The two fairy bluebirds are larger species, about 10 inches long, one ranging from India to Indochina and Malaya, the other limited to the Philippines. The males are handsome black birds with bright-blue mantles, the females much duller. Recent skeletal studies suggest they are misplaced in this family, and may be more closely related to the forest orioles.

Like the leafbirds and orioles, fairy bluebirds live in the forest crown and feed largely on fruit. They are particularly fond of wild figs, and also eat some flower nectar. While not migratory, they wander locally depending on the seasonal abundance of fruit. They usually travel quietly in pairs through the forest, but when a large fig tree is bearing, scores of birds may gather for the banquet together with orioles, leafbirds, hornbills, bulbuls, and other fruiteaters, drawn by the same magnet.

Fairy bluebirds build rather frail saucer nests of twigs and moss, usually in saplings or thin bushes deep in the forest gloom. They normally lay two greenish-white eggs heavily marked with brown splotches.

DIPPERS

PASSERIFORMES CINCLIDAE

The only truly aquatic passerines are the dippers, whose habitat and mode of life are shared by no other bird. Dippers live only on cool, clear, rushing mountain streams. Their element is the spray-drenched rocks where the roar of the water fills one's ears. This environment has become their very own. They go in and out of the water with gay abandon, and walk into it and under the surface with utter unconcern.

The four species of dippers are all similar in size, structure, and habits, and are all placed in the single genus *Cinclus*. The uniform brownish-gray North American Dipper lives in our western mountains from Alaska to Panama. The White-headed Dipper ranges down the Andes from Colombia to northern Argentina. The Common Dipper of Europe, brown with a white throat and breast, lives on mountain streams from Scandinavia to northwest Africa and eastward to the Himalayas. The all-brown Asiatic Dipper is spread across Siberia and China, north to Kamchatka and south to Formosa.

Just where and from what ancestral passerine stock dippers developed is uncertain. One school holds they evolved in central Asia from some thrushlike forebear and invaded the New World via the good old Bering land bridge. In support of this theory is the dippers' thrushlike tarsus and the mottled breasts of the immature birds in the Old World species. It seems more likely, however, that the dippers arose in the western American Cordilleras from a wrenlike ancestor and worked their way westward into Eurasia. They show more similarities to the wrens than to the thrushes—in their nesting habits as well as in their short stubby wings and tails, thick brownish plumage, and distinctive musty body odor. The dippers are unquestionably a relatively ancient group.

Chief among dippers' unique adaptations to their unparalleled way of life are their soft, filmy plumage with a very thick undercoat of down and their tremendous preen gland, ten times the size of that of any other passerine bird. The gland provides the oil to keep their feathers waterproof. Other structural modifications are a movable flap over the nostrils (to keep out water) and a highly developed nictitating membrane, or third eyelid, which they use for keeping their eyes clear of droplets in the splashing spray of falls and rapids.

Dippers have stout, strong legs and feet, but their toes

are not webbed. They do not swim well on the surface, but pitch along with a jerky motion until their feet hit bottom. They swim expertly under water, using their wings for propulsion, and have been known to fly down through 20 feet of water to feed on the bottom. The length of their average dive is about 10 seconds, with a probable maximum of perhaps 30 seconds. Whether or not they actually walk on the bottom is debatable. As their specific gravity is much lower than that of water, they cannot stay on the bottom without exerting some force to keep them from bobbing up to the surface. Their wings doubtless help keep them under, but it is also thought they set the angle of their bodes against the current to plane down, a possible reason why they prefer fast running streams.

Dippers fly straight and fast with a quail-like buzzing of their stubby wings, usually close to the water. They seldom fly far, and are quite sedentary. Dippers are solitary birds, seen in one another's company only at nesting time. Each individual or pair seems to occupy its own half mile or mile of stream, where they remain the year round unless forced to move by the drying up or freezing over of the waters. Cold does not seem to bother them, for they play merrily along the mountain torrents, even when the surrounding country-side is blanketed deep in snow.

Dippers feed mainly on water insects. They pick adult may-flies, stoneflies, and caddisflies from along the banks, and seek out their larvae among the rocks and gravel of the stream bed. Nor do they disdain other small aquatic life such as newts and minnows. They are so fond of fingerlings and trout fry that they become real nuisances around fish hatcheries.

The dippers' call and alarm note is a sharp piercing "djii" that carries clear and far above the roar of the waters. They also have a lovely, burbling wrenlike song that they sing throughout the year except during the postnuptial molting season in late summer and early fall. The song is not so loud and piercing as the call note, and difficult to hear except when sung in the quiet reaches of some backwater.

In their nesting habits the dippers are very wrenlike. They

build large domed nests of moss, sometimes lined with grass and leaves, and always with a side entrance. The nest is usually hidden in rock crevices, or between tree roots, close to the water. Protected ledges and nooks behind waterfalls are favorite sites. The clutch is 3 to 6, usually 4 or 5, pure-white eggs which the female incubates alone for the 16 days it takes them to hatch. Both parents feed the young, though the female seems to do most of the work. The young remain in the nest 15 to 24 days, and the moment they leave are as much at home in the water as their parents, walking into it immediately with the same facility and unconcern. Dippers nest early in the spring and usually rear at least two broods each year.

COMMON DIPPER
Cinclus cinclus
Europe to Himalayas   7 in.

NORTH AMERICAN DIPPER
Cinclus mexicanus
Alaska to Panama   8 in.

WRENS

Few small birds are as unmistakable as the familiar, busy brown wrens—the small birds with the big voices. Few have a firmer niche in men's hearts and folklore and legend than the bird we call the Winter Wren and which the English have known simply as The Wren since early Anglo-Saxon days. In English nursery tales the wren is traditionally feminine, and given such endearing titles as Jenny Wren or Kitty Wren. Continental folklore makes the wren masculine, as in the German "Zaunkönig," king of the hedges, and the Dutch "Winterkoning." The French "troglodyte mignon," or little cave dweller, also masculine, is reflected in its scientific name, *Troglodytes*. This derives partly from the large covered nest the wren makes, partly from its habitual skulking and roosting in rock crevices and root tangles.

How the tiny wren won its legendary position as king of the birds is one of the oldest of European folk tales. At a caucus to decide which should be their ruler, the birds agreed that the title should go to the one that flew the highest. The eagle promptly soared above all the others, but when he was about to proclaim his majesty from the heights, a little wren that had stowed away unnoticed on his back flew up a few feet higher and trilled out his triumph to the world below. The wren was used symbolically as king of the birds in medieval feasts and celebrations, some of which persist to this day in rural parts of Europe and the British Isles.

The Wren, the traditional king of the birds, is, oddly enough, the only member of an extensive New World family found outside the Americas. How long ago it invaded Eurasia, probably via Alaska, we have no way of knowing. Its remains have been found in Pleistocene deposits in Europe, and the species has been in Eurasia long enough to differentiate into

26 distinct geographical races. The Wren occurs south to Formosa, northern India, and northwest Africa, and populations are resident on the Hebrides, Shetland, and Faroe islands, and in Iceland. In North America the same species (our Winter Wren) breeds across the Canadian woodlands from Alaska to Newfoundland and south in the mountains to California and Georgia. Here we have 8 geographical races, 5 of them on various islets in the Aleutians. These island populations do not migrate, but the continental Winter Wrens winter southward to the Gulf of Mexico.

The most recent revision of the wren family lists 59 species divided among 14 genera and ranging from Canada southward to the tip of South America and out into the Falkland Islands. Wrens are most abundant and diversified in Central and South America. Strangely, the family is almost absent from the West Indies. The House Wren has extended its range northward from South America through the Lesser Antilles as far as Dominica. The only other wren known from the islands is the Zapata Wren, which undoubtedly has the most restricted range of any American bird. It is known to live only in one swamp, scarcely 5 square miles in area, on the south coast of Cuba, where it was discovered in 1926. The Zapata Wren resembles Bewick's Wren of North America. These little wrens never leave Zapata Swamp, but hide in its dense scrub. When they fly, which is seldom, they only flutter weakly for a few feet.

The 59 wrens form one of the better defined and cohesive of the passerine families. Their distribution shows them unquestionably of Western Hemisphere origin, but their ancestry is obscure. Their closest ties are to the dippers and to the mockingbirds. All three groups probably stemmed originally from some primitive insect-eating oscine of early Tertiary time that was probably akin to the ancestor of the thrushes.

All the wrens are similar in appearance and are easily recognizable as wrens. Most are less than 6 inches long and the largest barely reaches 9 inches. All are soberly dressed in browns or brownish grays, variously striped, streaked, spotted, or mottled with black, gray, white, or contrasting shades of brown. The sexes are alike. All have slender, sharp-pointed bills, which vary from short to fairly long, usually slightly down-curved. All have comparatively large, stout legs and feet and short rounded wings. Wrens fly rather weakly, but have a quick, straight, buzzing flight. They characteristically carry their stubby tails cocked bolt upright.

Most wrens live close to the ground in the tangled underbrush where they search for insects. They are adaptable little mites and have successfully invaded many habitats. The Cactus and the Rock wrens are at home on dry, treeless mountain slopes. The Short-billed and the Long-billed marsh wrens spend their lives in the reeds and cattails of salt- and fresh-water marshes. The White-breasted and Gray-breasted wood wrens live on the floor of tropical forests from southern Mexico to Bolivia. Others, like the House, Bewick's, Winter, and Carolina wrens, live in garden shrubbery and hedgerows, and nest around houses and outbuildings.

Wrens are highly vocal. They may be hard to see as they scamper through brush piles, scurry mouselike among tree roots, or hide in tangled swamp sedges, but they invariably betray their presence with their harsh, chattering, scolding calls. Almost all are fine singers that delight the ear with intricate burbling melodies, which seem much too loud and rich to come from such small throats. Both sexes sing, and they sing practically throughout the year, which may be a way pairs keep in contact with one another in impenetrable habitats where vision is limited. Some tropical wrens sing antiphonal duets between pairs, one bird singing the first few notes, its mate finishing the strophe.

Wrens build large bulky nests, which typically are domed with a side entrance, and are mostly the work of the male. Male wrens have such a strong urge to build nests that each usually builds several in his territory, sometimes as many as half a dozen. This is evidently an integral part of nuptial display and courtship. The female selects one of the nests for the brood—one perhaps meant for the purpose, for it is

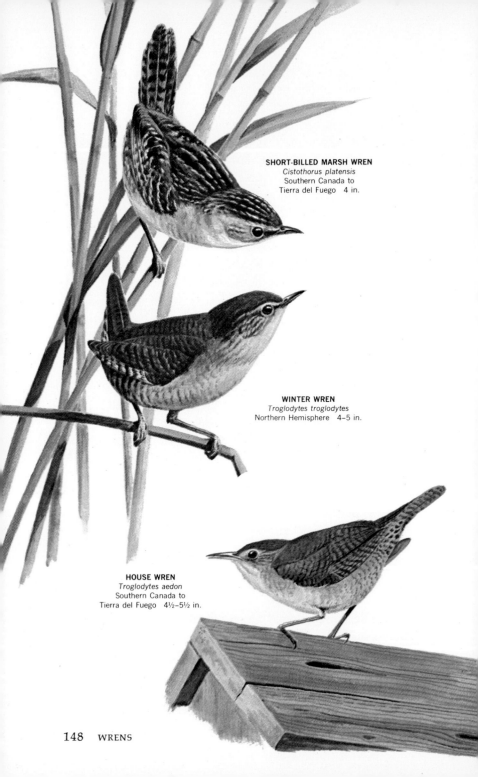

SHORT-BILLED MARSH WREN
Cistothorus platensis
Southern Canada to
Tierra del Fuego   4 in.

WINTER WREN
Troglodytes troglodytes
Northern Hemisphere   4–5 in.

HOUSE WREN
Troglodytes aedon
Southern Canada to
Tierra del Fuego   4½–5½ in.

usually better built and better hidden than the others. The female lines this nest and finishes it for occupancy. The extra "cock nests" are usually flimsy structures and poorly, if at all, concealed. The cock often sleeps in one or another of them. Another purpose these dummy nests may serve is to fool cowbirds into laying in them instead of in the real nest.

Many wrens are cavity nesters, and these will use almost any natural hole they find on or near the ground—tangled roots, clefts in rocks, and abandoned woodpecker holes. The Winter Wren's favorite site is among the upturned roots of a fallen tree. Other cavity-nesting species, Bewick's Wren and the Carolina Wren among them, find sites around dwellings. Most familiar of these is the common House Wren, a widespread species of 30-odd races which ranges from southern Canada south to Cape Horn and the Falkland Islands. The House Wren is one of the most frequent users of bird boxes wherever people put them up. The House Wren isn't particular, and almost any bird box will do, provided the entrance is large enough for it to enter. The minimum diameter, the size of a 25-cent piece, keeps out House Sparrows, but House Wrens prefer wider holes that let them lug in larger sticks. If several houses are put up near one another the male defending the territory will, in true wren fashion, fill most of them with debris. If houses aren't available, the House Wren will use holes in trees and stumps, empty tin cans, rural mail boxes and old wasp's nests. It may also use the space behind a loose board in an outbuilding or under the dashboard of an unused carriage, tractor, or piece of farm machinery.

Wrens are generally multibrooded, and some are polygamous. Incubation is usually by the female alone. The male sometimes feeds her on the nest, and he helps rear the young. The eggs vary from pure white to dark brown, and are often speckled. Clutches range from 2 or 3 in most tropical forms to 8 or 10 in some temperate zone species. The House Wren usually lays 4 to 6 speckled white eggs and incubates 12 to 15 days, averaging 14. The nestling period varies from 12 to 18 days, depending on the size of the brood and how well

CACTUS WREN
Campylorhynchus brunneicapillus
Western United States
and Mexico 8 in.

ZAPATA WREN
Ferminia cerverai
Cuba 6¼ in.

the young are fed. Usually the smaller the brood, the more food each nestling gets, and the quicker it grows.

Except for a few tropical species that are slightly gregarious when not nesting, wrens are typically solitary and do not form flocks. They like to roost under cover at night, and when away from their nests will creep into crevices and crannies to sleep. They have been found dozing in scarecrows and in pockets of shirts hung on clotheslines.

MOCKINGBIRDS, CATBIRDS, AND THRASHERS

PASSERIFORMES   MIMIDAE

An even more thoroughly American family than the wrens, and closely allied to them, are the 31 species of mockingbirds and their relatives, the catbirds and thrashers. All these birds are fine singers and most are excellent mimics, the mockingbirds especially so—hence their family name of Mimidae. One occasionally hears them referred to collectively as the "mimine thrushes." They probably developed, as did the wrens, from some thrushlike ancestor.

In many ways the Mimidae are intermediate between the wrens and the thrushes. Their nesting habits are distinctly thrushlike in that they build open cup nests. In other behavioral features and in color pattern they resemble the wrens. The thrashers, in particular, look and act like overgrown wrens. Medium-sized birds from 8 to 12 inches in length, the mimids are more slenderly built than thrushes and have longer tails, and slender, more wrenlike bills. The sexes are alike. All are active, inquisitive, aggressive birds that live near the ground and eat insects, fruit, and berries.

Most famous of the family is the Mockingbird of the southern United States, which is as symbolic of the Old South as magnolias, hominy, "chitlins," and mint juleps. Selected as "state bird" by five Southern states—Tennessee, Arkansas, Florida, Mississippi, and Texas—the Mockingbird has earned this perhaps empty and unrewarding honor by its vocal powers and its conspicuousness. Mockingbirds draw attention to themselves not only by their wonderful singing, but by their constant activity and their staunch defense of their territories against intruders. They love to chivy the household cat or dog.

Mockingbirds sing almost throughout the year, and usually pick an exposed place to sing from, a roof eave, telephone wire, or the top of a fencepost. They pour forth their matchless melodies at odd times throughout the day and often sing at night when the moon is full. Then, when other bird voices are stilled and the noises of civilization quiet down, their song is heard at its best. While Mockingbirds have burbling wrenlike songs of their own, most of their melodies are imitations of the sounds of other birds they have heard. Typically they repeat each phrase three or four times before changing tune.

Individual mockers have been credited with rendering perfect imitations of the songs of 30 or more different species in succession, and with giving recognizable replicas of such unbirdlike sounds as the postman's whistle and a squeaking cart wheel. They are quick to pick up any new song they hear and add it to their repertoire. When caged Nightingales were brought from Europe and housed in the gardens of the Bok Singing Tower in Florida, the local Mockingbirds were soon singing the same lovely liquid notes. Sound spectrograph records of the Mockingbirds' versions compared with the original Nightingale songs show them to be exact reproductions of each phrase in all its parts, including vibrations beyond the range of the human ear.

The Mockingbird builds a stout, cup-shaped nest of short, stiff twigs lined with grasses and rootlets, usually well hidden in the shrubbery or the lower branches of a tree, seldom less than 3 or more than 20 feet above the ground. Both sexes bring material and work hard enough to finish the nest in 3 or 4 days, sometimes by dint of excess zeal in as little as 2 days. The clutch is 3 to 6 greenish eggs spotted with redbrown. Incubation is mainly by the female, though the male may take a short stint on the eggs during her absence. Incubation takes 12 to 14 days, and both parents feed the young. The fledglings mature rapidly and are often able to leave the nest in another fortnight. Hence the entire breeding cycle is seldom more than a month. Pairs usually raise two or more broods each year.

The common Mockingbird is the northernmost of nine similar species assigned to the genus *Mimus* which range from the central United States southward through the West Indies and Central America to Argentina and Chile. All are slim, slender birds, gray to gray-brown above, lighter below, and usually with white or pale-gray markings in the wings and tail. One species, with a larger bill and legs and narrower nostrils that justify placing it in a genus of its own, *Nesomimus*, is resident in the Galapagos Islands. The two Blue

MOCKINGBIRD
Mimus polyglottos
Southern U.S. and Mexico   10½ in.

BLUE MOCKINGBIRD
Melanotis caerulescens
Mexico   10 in.

BROWN THRASHER
Toxostoma rufum
Eastern U.S. and
southern Canada   12 in.

CATBIRD
Dumetella carolinensis
Southern Canada to
Gulf States   9 in.

Mockingbirds of Mexico are an exception to the family's dull colors. One is solid blue; the other has a white belly. Like their gray relatives, the Blue Mockingbirds are notable singers and good mimics.

One of the most distinctive members of the family, and the least variable, is the friendly gray Catbird, unmistakable for its black cap and russet undertail coverts, and its feline mewing call. While no vocal match for the Mockingbird, the Catbird has a pleasant song and ventures some imitations, which are not as loud, accurate, or varied as the mocker's, though recognizable for what they are meant to be. Also, the Catbird never repeats its phrases.

Like the Mockingbird, the Catbird likes to live around houses and becomes very tame. It builds a similar cup nest of twigs in the shrubbery and lays 4 to 6 glossy, greenish-blue eggs, which take 12 to 13 days to hatch. While primarily insectivorous, the Catbird consumes quantities of berries and small fruits, and is occasionally accused of raiding grapevines and blackberry patches. These depredations are seldom serious, and most country folk and suburbanites regard the Catbird as a pleasant neighbor and are glad to see it return in the spring.

The Catbird breeds across most of North America from southern Canada southward to the northern edge of the Gulf States. It winters from the southern states through the West Indies and Central America to Panama. A small population resident in Bermuda is inseparable from the mainland Catbirds. A close relative is the Black Catbird of Yucatán and British Honduras, exactly like the Catbird in size, shape, and habits, but glossy black in color.

The thrashers are a more varied group of slightly larger birds with noticeably long tails. Most of them are brownish above and have white breasts and bellies streaked with brown. Ten of the 17 species are grouped in the genus *Toxostoma*, typical and best known of which is the Brown Thrasher, a common resident of most of the eastern and central parts of the United States. The Brown Thrasher is less companionable than the Catbird and Mockingbird. It lives in the wilder copses and forest edges and searches through the undergrowth and ground litter for its food. Its song is louder than that of the Catbird, and it makes no attempt at mimicry. While it occasionally sings from an exposed perch, it sings more often from cover, and its song is easily recognized by the bird's tendency to repeat each phrase twice.

Eight other species of thrashers are found in the western United States and southward into Central America. Largest of the family is the 12-inch California Thrasher, a tawny bird that feeds largely on the ground in chaparral country and in mixed brushlands, avoiding the solid forests. The Sage Thrasher, the Crissal Thrasher, and the Le Conte's Thrasher inhabit the more arid regions of the West, feed largely on the ground, and usually nest in thorny cactus or stiff-twigged desert brush.

Four species of thrashers are limited to the West Indies. Two of them are exceedingly rare and in danger of extinction. The White-breasted Thrasher, brownish above and white below, occurs only on the islands of Martinique and Saint Lucia and is seldom reported nowadays. It is wrenlike in its actions and it chatters and cocks its tail as it moves about the underbrush.

Another rare species is the Trembler, a ground forest dweller of the smaller islands, now extirpated from most of its former haunts. This species' peculiar habit of shivering and trembling has never been satisfactorily explained. The decline of both the Trembler and the White-breasted Thrasher has resulted from human persecution, from the cutting of forest cover, and from introduced predators.

The Scaly-breasted Thrasher of the Lesser Antilles and the Pearly-eyed Thrasher, which ranges from the Bahamas south to many islands in the southern Caribbean, are not as rare, possibly because they are tree dwellers, less molested by rats and other introduced predators. These island thrashers have low reproductive rates. They lay only 2 to 3 eggs per clutch, against double that number in the mainland species.

TOWNSEND'S SOLITAIRE
Myadestes townsendi
Western North America   9 in.

ORANGE-BILLED NIGHTINGALE-THRUSH
Catharus aurantiirostris
Mexico to Venezuela   6½ in.

THRUSHES

PASSERIFORMES   TURDIDAE

In this large family are some of the most highly regarded songbirds in the world. The thrushes are such renowned songsters that the name has become a common synonym for a singer. No other family has so many members famed for their music—the Nightingale, Song Thrush, Hermit Thrush, Wood Thrush, to name but a few. Other well-known thrushes, loved for their beauty as well as their song, include the robins and bluebirds. Less familiar groups are the solitaires, chats, wheatears, shortwings, cochoas, and forktails. Still others have no common names.

The thrush family is practically cosmopolitan, absent only

from the Antarctic, the frigid parts of the Arctic, some Polynesian islands, and from New Zealand (where the European Blackbird and Song Thrush were successfully introduced in 1862). The family has its greatest development in the temperate and tropical regions of the Old World, where it is believed to have originated. If so, its conquest of the New World must have occurred very early, for a number of thrush groups are thoroughly established and well developed in North and South America and in the West Indies.

The thrush's closest relatives are two other equally large families of predominantly Old World birds, the warblers and the flycatchers. All three are fairly generalized, insect-eating oscines with 10 primary feathers on each wing. While most members of these three families—Turdidae, Sylviidae, and Muscicapidae—can be assigned to their respective families with little trouble, the lines between the three are not sharp. The number of borderline species difficult to assign to one or another confirm their close relationships. The differences between them are so slight they are sometimes considered subfamilies of a single family. As the three groups contain more than a thousand species, almost one-eighth of the world's birds, the tendency today is to give family rank to each.

The thrushes are slightly larger, chunkier birds than the Old World warblers and the flycatchers, and typically have the tarsus unscaled or "booted." Though essentially insectivorous, thrushes do not catch insects in flight. They feed on the ground as well as in trees, and eat more vegetable food, particularly fruit, than warblers and flycatchers do. All build open cup nests, usually in trees or bushes, some on the ground, and a few in rock crevices and tree cavities.

Being stronger fliers and perhaps more vigorous and adaptable, the thrushes have been more successful than the warblers and flycatchers in spreading over the world. Thrushes colonized the New World in several invasions, and populations have reached and settled many oceanic islands—Tristan da Cunha in mid-South Atlantic, the Hawaiian and Bonin islands, and the West Indies. Many of these small island populations became so specialized that when man arrived and changed their environment they disappeared rapidly. Several Hawaiian and West Indian thrushes have vanished within the last half century. The Bonin Island Thrush has not been seen since four specimens were collected in 1828. The species was probably wiped out shortly thereafter by rats that escaped from whaling ships.

The 307 species currently assigned to the thrush family are divided among 49 genera. The most widespread and best known of these is the nominate genus *Turdus,* to which 61 species are ascribed. These are the largest members of the thrush family, medium-sized birds from 8 to 12 inches in length. As typical as any is the American Robin, one of the most familiar dooryard birds of temperate North America. The American Robin is one of the most companionable of our thrushes, and replaces the swallow as the traditional herald of spring in North America. Its "cheerily-cheerily-cheerily," full-throated and sweet, means spring is really here in New England.

The Robin breeds across North America from the tree line southward to the southern United States and winters from the Gulf States southward into Central America. Normally a bird of sparse woodlands, forest edges, and open scrublands, it has found the changes brought by civilization much to its liking, and now nests more commonly near dwellings in cultivated lands and city suburbs than it does in uninhabited regions. It builds its well-formed open nest of straw and other fibers reinforced with mud usually in a shrub or tree from 5 to 30 feet up, often in a sheltered recess on a building. Nest building and incubation are almost entirely by the female. The clutch of four clear blue-green eggs takes 12 to 14 days to hatch, and the young fledge in another 2 weeks. The male stands by and helps guard the nest and feed the young. The Robin is multibrooded except in the North, where the summers are too short.

A typical thrush, the Robin eats a varied menu of insects, small fruits, and berries. The Robin's diet is roughly 60 per cent vegetable, most of this small fruits. Stories of Robins getting tipsy from eating overripe wild cherries are quite true, fortuitous intemperance being a weakness it shares with many fruit-eating birds. Less than a century ago Robins were shot for sport and for food in this country, as some of their relatives still are elsewhere. They were sold in eastern U.S. markets for 60 cents a dozen as recently as 1913. Most Americans today would as soon think of eating the family dog.

The Robin's popularity and adaptability seemed, until recently, to assure its perpetuation as a favorite songbird. Its existence is now threatened seriously by the wholesale broadcasting of new powerful insecticides, whose residual effects, long after they have stopped working on the insects, kill birds. As the rains wash DDT into the soil, it impregnates earthworms. These come to the surface where Robins eat them and die. Municipalities that fog their residential areas regularly with DDT have witnessed marked declines in Robin populations. Some Midwestern cities have succeeded in wiping these birds out entirely.

Though the Robin is the only *Turdus* in North America, the genus has established itself firmly to the southward. More than a score of other turdine species live in the West Indies and from Mexico southward throughout South America to Tierra del Fuego and the Falkland Islands. Gray's Thrush of Central America and northern South America is one example, and the White-chinned Thrush of Jamaica another. The tropical forms are usually resident; those breeding at higher latitudes and altitudes move with the seasons.

The genus *Turdus* is best developed in the Old World. Among the Robin's closest relatives abroad is the European Blackbird, the male resembling an all-black Robin with a yellow bill. The female is a nondescript brown. The Blackbird hops over the green British lawns just as our Robin does in America, and sings the same sort of melodious spring song from a conspicuous perch. The European Blackbird has long been a gourmets' favorite, as the old nursery rhyme "four-and-twenty blackbirds baked in a pie" attests.

Other European turdine species worthy of mention are the Ring Ouzel, a black thrush marked with a white chest band and common in higher country; the sweet-singing Song Thrush; the Mistle Thrush, named for its fondness for mistletoe berries; the Fieldfare, which has recently established itself in Greenland; and the Redwing. Almost a score more are found in Asia—the Siberian Red-throated, Black-throated, Eyebrowed, Dusky, and Naumann's thrushes among the better known. All these Eurasian thrushes are similar to the American Robin in the essential features of their habits and behavior. All are migratory; they travel and winter similarly in loose flocks, sometimes of considerable size, and usually congregate where berries are plentiful.

A distinctive group of North American thrushes are the

WOOD THRUSH
Hylocichla mustelina
Eastern North America   8 in.

NIGHTINGALE
Luscinia megarhynchos
Europe, southwestern Asia   6½ in.

HERMIT THRUSH
Hylocichla guttata
North America   7 in.

EUROPEAN BLACKBIRD
Turdus merula
Europe, North Africa,
south-central Asia   10 in.

five species of *Hylocichlas*, the Wood, Hermit, Swainson's, and Gray-cheeked thrushes, and the Veery. Slightly smaller than most of the *Turdus* group, these North American thrushes are uniformly brown above and white below, and have spotted breasts. All are forest inhabitants that search the forest floor for grubs, insects, fruits, berries, and leaf buds. Swainson's and the Gray-cheeked thrushes breed in the Canadian zone evergreen forests. The Hermit Thrush breeds across northern North America in mixed woodlands. The Veery summers in deciduous forests, as does the Wood Thrush of the eastern United States, the only one of the group that commonly nests in suburban shrubbery.

These forest thrushes are all fine singers. Their voices are somewhat similar, but each species pipes a distinctive pattern

EASTERN BLUEBIRD ♂
Sialia sialis
Eastern North America 7 in.

WHITE-RUMPED ♂
SHAMA
Copsychus malabaricus
India to Indochina
and East Indies 11 in.

EUROPEAN REDSTART
Phoenicurus phoenicurus
Europe to central Asia 5½ in.

AMERICAN ROBIN
Turdus migratorius
North America 10 in.

EUROPEAN ROBIN
Erithacus rubecula
Europe, Asia Minor 5½ in.

**BLUE (RED-BELLIED)
ROCK THRUSH** ♂
Monticola solitarius
Southern Eurasia,
to Japan 9 in.

of song that plays an essential part in territorial relationships and courtship. All build well-formed, cup-shaped nests of twigs, grasses, and leaves, often strengthened with mud. The Veery and the Hermit Thrush usually nest on the ground, the other three in shrubs and low trees, seldom more than 10 feet up. All lay 3 to 4 eggs, greenish blue in color, sometimes spotted with brown, which are incubated entirely by the female, the male standing by to help feed the young. The Wood and Hermit thrushes winter to the Gulf States and Mexico, the other three species travel on to northern South America.

In Central America and northern South America are seven species of the genus *Catharus* known as nightingale thrushes, whose habits and behavior are so similar to those of the *Hylocichla* group that some consider them congeneric. The nightingale thrushes have largely lost the spotting of the breast and are nonmigratory, but they are ground-feeding forest dwellers and sing the same sort of bell-like songs.

The three American bluebirds of the genus *Sialia* are typified by the familiar Eastern Bluebird with its blue back and reddish breast. The Western Bluebird and the Mountain Bluebird are similar 6- to 7-inch birds that have replaced the red on the breast with blue or white. Bluebirds are gentle birds whose soft warbling songs are neither as loud nor as impressive as those of other thrushes. Partial to open woodlands, they are cavity nesters. Bluebirds nest in natural tree holes and often occupy bird boxes, in which they build a typical thrush cup nest. Bluebirds raise 2 and sometimes 3 broods in a season. The female does all the incubating; the male helps rear the young. After the young have flown, the parents often pick new mates for the next brood.

The solitaires (*Myadestes*) are a group of seven largely tropical American thrushes found from Mexico and the West Indies southward through Brazil. Townsend's Solitaire, the only temperate zone member of the group, breeds in the western mountains from Mexico north to Alaska. Solitaires are rather shy, trim, plain-colored birds, difficult to see in their forest homes. Their colors are mostly olive-brown to gray, the bills are always black, and the tails are usually longer in relation to the body than those of the other American thrushes and are frequently edged with white. As befits members of the thrush family, solitaires are outstanding singers, and their flutelike melodies, unhurried and simple, are among the loveliest of tropical bird songs.

Oddest of the New World thrushes is the tiny Wrenthrush (*Zeledonia*), a shy resident of the high mountain forests above 5,000 feet in Costa Rica and western Panama. It creeps and hops around, wren fashion, on the forest floor. The Wrenthrush is unique among thrushes in having its 10th primary so greatly shortened that some students put the bird in a family by itself. Its voice is reported as a clear, musical whistle repeated 6 or 8 times at equal intervals. In its short tail and short, rounded wings it seems most closely related to the shortwings (*Brachypteryx*), a small group of six Asiatic thrushes ranging from the Himalayas across southern China to the Philippines and southward through the East Indies to Java. The shortwings are also wrenlike birds of forest thickets at high altitudes, but unlike the Wrenthrush, the shortwing sexes differ in color.

Among the more distinctive of the many Old World thrush groups are the nine rock thrushes of the genus *Monticola*. These are medium-sized thrushes 8 to 9 inches in length found widely over Eurasia and Africa. Most of them are blue with some admixture of browns and reds. As the name implies, they are partial to open rocky country. Most of them, like the Blue Rock Thrush of Eurasia, are mountain dwellers living in rocky gorges, stony cliffs, and boulder-clad hillsides. They are not gregarious, but are usually encountered in pairs or small family groups. Some of these birds are also at home on sea coasts.

The Red-bellied Rock Thrush of eastern Asia is one of the few passerine species that has adapted itself completely to a beach life. It perches on the boulders in the salt spray on the rocky shores of Japan and Korea and feeds among the kelp and seaweed exposed at low tide. It is seldom found inland, but is a common dooryard bird in coastal fishing villages. It builds its typical thrush nest of grasses and rootlets in a crevice in the rocks at the edge of the beach and lays 4 to 5 clear pale-blue eggs.

Another outstanding Eastern Hemisphere group is formed by the 18 wheatears (*Oenanthe*). Wheatears are thrushes that have left the woodlands and live mostly in open country, bare hillsides, coastal downs and dunelands, and in deserts of Eurasia and Africa. All are dapper ground birds from 5 to 7 inches long, often attractively marked with contrasting black and white. Most species have black facial markings, black on the wings and tail, and a distinctive white rump. The name "Wheatear" has nothing to do with wheat or ear, but is a euphemism for the Anglo-Saxon "white arse." The common Wheatear is widespread across the northern

STONECHAT
Saxicola torquata
Eurasia, Africa, Madagascar 5 in.

WHEATEAR
Oenanthe oenanthe
Eurasia, Alaska, Labrador,
Baffin Is., Greenland, Iceland 6 in.

Palearctic and breeds in the tundras of Greenland, north-eastern Canada, and western Alaska. It winters southward to Africa. When wheatears flock to migrate southward, they are usually very fat. For years, they have been a gourmets' favorite. In parts of Europe and Africa they are still netted for market.

The Old World is also the home of a large complex of small thrushes of several genera, most of them less than 7 inches in length, sometimes called collectively the "chat thrushes" from their tendency to chatter and scold. Here are grouped some of the most familiar of European birds, the original Robin and such appropriately named birds as the Whinchat (which lives in whins—wet grassy meadows) and the Stonechat, which lives in neglected gorse country and old pastures and has a call note like two stones clicked together. Here are the descriptively named Bluethroat and

BLUETHROAT
Erithacus svecicus
Eurasia   5½ in.

WREN-THRUSH
Zeledonia coronata
Costa Rica and Panama   4½ in.

Rubythroat, and the original Redstart (not to be confused with the unrelated American Redstart, a wood warbler). Here also are such notable singers as the White-rumped Shama and the Dyal Thrush of India, and the most famed singer of all, the Nightingale.

The Robin of legend and story is a small, plump, friendly bird, which is common about gardens, hedgerows, and farmyards throughout Europe and the British Isles. The English have always thought so highly of the Robin they carried the name wherever they went and gave it to foreign species that reminded them of their familiar homeland bird. So we find robins, related and unrelated, the world around, in America, Australia, India, Africa—wherever English is spoken.

The Robin's appeal stems from its engaging manners and friendly tameness. While it is a good singer, its voice is not as outstanding as those of the Nightingales and many other thrushes. It chatters and scolds a great deal, and its song, while not loud, is varied and musical, and has a melancholy quality.

Most of the chat thrushes are birds of open woodlands and brushy fields and most of them nest on or near the ground. A few, such as the Redstart, are cavity nesters. Their eggs are usually pale-green to blue, and may or may not be spotted. Those of the Robin are white with fine brown speckling. All lay slightly larger clutches than the bigger thrushes do, usually from 5 to 6 eggs. Their breeding patterns are likewise much the same, with the female assuming most or all of the nest-building and incubating duties, the male encouraging her with his singing, and standing by to help feed the young. Incubation and fledging times run 12 to 15 days. Many of the chat thrushes are multibrooded, and the male sometimes takes complete charge of the first brood when the female starts incubating her second clutch.

In addition to their chattering, the chat thrushes sing fairly complex melodies, which they deliver with energy and enthusiasm. This is particularly true of the Nightingale, whose vigorous song seems much too loud to come from so small a bird. The Nightingale is unimpressive in appearance, a nondescript plain brown above and white below. It acts much like the Robin and frequents the same surroundings, but is shier and seldom comes out of the undergrowth to feed in the open. It usually sings from cover and, despite its name and reputation, sings more freely during daylight than at night. It does sing habitually at night, however, and its song is most impressive in the quiet of the moonlight, when other voices and noises are stilled. Its song is exceptionally rich and varied. Pleasing and melodious though the Nightingale's song is, I have always been impressed more by its strength and vigor than by its beauty.

OLD WORLD WARBLERS

PASSERIFORMES   SYLVIIDAE

With a few exceptions the 415 species gathered in this tremendous family are small, dull-colored, active birds with thin bills and rather weak legs and feet. The sexes are usually alike or similar in color. Old World warblers differ from thrushes and Old World flycatchers principally in having unspotted young. The tarsus may be either scaled or booted, and rictal bristles may be well developed or absent. These warblers are not to be confused with New World, or wood, warblers, which are a totally unrelated group of birds having only 9 instead of 10 functional primary feathers and differing in other structural features and in habits.

The family Sylviidae is something of a catchall. As currently assayed, it consists of four subfamilies, each of which some students regard as worth family rank. These are the Sylviinae, or true warblers, of the Old World; the Polioptilinae, or gnatcatchers, of the New World; the Regulinae, or kinglets, of panboreal distribution in the Northern Hemisphere; and the aberrant Malurinae, or Australian warblers, limited to Australia, New Zealand, and the East Indies.

In addition to their similar structural characteristics, members of each of these subfamilies show fairly close affinities in habits and behavior. All live primarily, some exclusively, on insects. Most are arboreal, though a few groups live in weedy swamps, grassy meadows, or brushlands. Song is well developed throughout the family and, though none is equal to the best thrushes, many Old World warblers are exceptional vocalists. The species of temperate distribution are mostly migratory, some of them highly so, while those of the tropics and subtropics tend to be sedentary. Old World warblers vary considerably in nesting habits. Most of them build an open cup nest, but many lay their eggs in a domed or covered one. Incubation may be by the female alone or by both sexes, but the pair bond is strong. When the female incubates alone, the male usually feeds her, and helps feed the young.

GREAT REED WARBLER
Acrocephalus arundinaceus
Central Eurasia,
Spain to Japan   7½ in.

PALLAS'S GRASSHOPPER WARBLER
Locustella certhiola
Western Siberia to Japan   5½ in.

**COMMON
FAN-TAILED WARBLER**
Cisticola juncidis
Southern Europe, Africa,
southeastern Asia   4 in.

BLACK-CAP
Sylvia atricapilla
Europe, western Asia   5½ in.

The true warblers, or Sylviinae, form by far the largest of the four subfamilies. They number about 316, or better than three-fourths of the family's species. The nominate genus *Sylvia* contains many common European birds, including such familiar species as the Garden Warbler, the Blackcap, and the White-throat. The Garden Warbler is a nondescript 5-inch bird, brownish above, pale-buffy below, that lives in the tangled forest undergrowth and skulks through hedgerows and shrubbery borders. All the members of the genus are active little birds that hunt for insects in this way, and all migrate southward in winter. All have rather monotonous, short, "tac-tac" call and alarm notes, and all have sweet, pleasant, warbling songs that make them as welcome in the garden as their insect-eating does. Their songs are usually distinctive and, as throughout this family of many closely similar species, the birds can often be told apart more easily by their songs. All the members of the genus *Sylvia* build open nests, usually fairly near the ground, in the shelter of bushes, brambles, or hedgerows. The males often make "cock nests" as do the wrens, either as an outlet for excess building drive, or for a roosting place, or to confuse predators and nest-parasitizing cuckoos. Both sexes incubate the 4 to 5 eggs, which take 11 to 12 days to hatch. The young usually remain in the nest another 9 to 10 days before fledging.

The some 30 species of leaf or willow warblers of the genus *Phylloscopus* that breed across temperate Eurasia and migrate

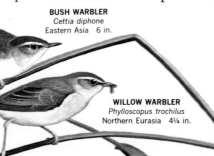

BUSH WARBLER
Cettia diphone
Eastern Asia   6 in.

WILLOW WARBLER
Phylloscopus trochilus
Northern Eurasia   4¼ in.

southward in winter to southern Asia and Africa are one of the most exasperating of all bird groups to identify in the field. One species, the Arctic Willow Warbler, has extended its breeding range across Bering Strait into Alaska. The only member of the subfamily to reach the New World, the Alaskan birds retrace their paths each autumn and migrate down the Asiatic coast to Indochina and the Philippines.

All the willow warblers are slim, greenish to greenish-yellow birds 4 to 5 inches in length. They lack distinctive field marks, and are hard to observe because they spend most of their time in the treetops hunting among the leaves for small insects. Field experts depend more on their songs and their actions to tell them apart than on their appearance. Their songs, while not impressive, are sweet, pleasing, musical warbles and are distinctive between species. One of the most distinctive songs is that of the Chiffchaff, one of the commoner European species. The song consists of two syllables, one higher than the other, repeated in irregular order: "chiff-chaff, chaff-chiff, chaff." Other species such as the Willow Warbler, the Greenish Warbler, and the Wood Warbler have characteristic combinations of trills and repeated notes that are easier to recognize than the little dull-colored bird uttering them from the treetops or the depths of a thicket.

Though all the willow warblers tend to feed in the higher foliage, all nest on or near the ground, and most of them build round domed nests with entrances on the side. Nest building and incubation are by the female alone. The eggs are white, lightly speckled with brown in some species, and usually number 6 to 7 in the first clutches. Second broods are generally smaller, from 4 to 5. Incubation is 12 to 13 days, and the young, fed by both parents, fledge in 13 to 15 days.

Nine species of rather plain, brownish warblers of the genus *Locustella* are known as grasshopper warblers because their thin, unimpressive buzzing songs seem more like the notes of an insect than those of a bird. The grasshopper warblers live in open brushlands, grassy meadows, and marshlands, and all are shy and hard to observe. During the breeding season the males perch momentarily on the tops of reed stems to sing their short, thin, little chirping songs, which are more like series of alarm notes. They stay in sight only a few moments while singing, then dive out of sight into the cover below.

Breeding patterns vary somewhat in the grasshopper warblers. All nest on or near the ground in thick cover. Some build a fragile open nest, others a closed one with a side entrance. Nest building and incubation may be by the female alone or by both parents. The eggs number 4 to 7, and are usually white with brown spottings. Incubation is usually 12 to 14 days; fledging takes another 10 to 15 days.

The dozen reed warblers of the genus *Acrocephalus* are another fairly distinct complex of warblers breeding across temperate Eurasia. Here again the species are so similar that their songs are more easily recognized than the birds themselves. Their voices are rather loud, and their songs are a strident but pleasant chattering that once heard can be easily re-identified. The song of the Great Reed Warbler, one of the larger members of the family, can be heard long distances over the marshes in summer. During the breeding season the reed warblers sing by night as well as by day.

Always found in marshes, as their name implies, the reed warblers hang their deep open nests on reed stems a few feet above the ground or water. Nest building is chiefly by the female, assisted in some species by the male, who usually also shares the incubation duties. The eggs may number 4 to 6 and are usually greenish to bluish, blotched or spotted with dark brown. In the Great Reed Warbler incubation is 14 to 15 days; the young leave the nest in another 12 days, but do not fly well for another 3 or 4 days. Both incubation and fledging times are shorter in the smaller species.

The fantail, or grass, warblers of the genus *Cisticola* are one of the most widespread of all the warbler groups. Some 75 species are recognized in this single genus, most of them in Africa, where they occupy many types of country, but always in or near grass. Other species are found from the Mediterranean region across Asia to Japan and southward to Australia. Some live in wet marshes, others in dry fields. All are little brown birds streaked above and lighter below, with rather broad, often light-tipped tails. All nest on or near the ground, some building an open cup, some a hanging purse, others a domed nest.

The Common Fan-tailed Warbler of Eurasia breeds in plainslands and grassy river bottoms. The male has an interesting song flight. Starting from its perch on a grass stem, it circles 50 to 100 feet in the air with a series of whistles which change to a guttural "dja-dja-dja" in its gradual fluttering descent. This species builds a bulky, bottle-shaped nest in the meadow grass, using slender leaves, rootlets, and the cottony flowers of marsh grasses which it weaves together with spider webs. Most *Cisticolas* line their nests with plant down and continue to add to them during incubation.

The most ingenious of all warbler nests are those built by the tailorbirds, nine species of which are found in southeast Asia from India to the Philippines and southward through the East Indies. A common and familiar bird of gardens and scrub country, the Long-tailed Tailorbird, the Darzee of Kipling's jungle tales, is one of the widest ranging, found from India eastward to southern China and southward to Java. Like all the tailorbirds, it is an unprepossessing little 4-inch skulker with a streaked olive-green back and a lighter belly. Thoroughly domesticated and not at all shy, it lives around human dwellings. Like most warblers it is extremely active and hops about the vines and bushes around the veranda in search of insects. It carries its tail cocked stiffly over its back wren-fashion, and jerks it up and down as it makes its short flights. Its shrill discordant calls are so loud and persistent they can become annoying on a hot day.

The tailorbird builds its nest within a cup made by sewing the edges of one or of two leaves together. It fills this cavity, lined with fine grasses and sometimes animal hairs, mainly with plant down. To sew the leaves together the bird first pierces holes in the leaf with the point of its beak and draws the thread through, knotting it on the outside enough to prevent its slipping back. Each stitch is made separately. For thread the tailorbird uses plant fibers or silk from insect cocoons or spider webs. The nests are usually within 6 feet of the ground, but may be considerably higher, the main requisite being the presence of leaves to be sewn together. Tailorbirds lay from 3 to 6 long pointed eggs which vary from buffy to greenish and are boldly spotted and splotched.

The five species of kinglets, three in the Old World, two in the New, all placed in the single genus *Regulus*, form a well-marked subfamily. Kinglets are tiny birds barely 4 inches in length with soft, fluffy olive or grayish-green plumage. All have brilliant, sometimes partly concealed crown patches of yellow to orange, except the American Ruby-crowned Kinglet, whose crown patch is bright red. These feathered mites are residents of the circumpolar conifer belt and nest from the tree limit southward in both hemispheres. The two American species breed side by side across the Canadian zone and southward at favorable altitudes in the western Cordilleras almost to the Mexican border. Both migrate in winter to the Gulf States, Mexico, and Guatemala.

LONG-TAILED TAILORBIRD
Orthotomus sutorius
India to southern China, Malaya, Java   5 in.

FORMOSAN KINGLET ♂
Regulus goodfellowi
Formosa   3½ in.

RUBY-CROWNED KINGLET ♂
Regulus calendula
Northern North America   4 in.

The Old World Goldcrest is so similar to our Golden-crowned Kinglet that some students regard the two as conspecific. The Goldcrest nests in the taiga zone of conifers southward to central Europe and Asia. Insular populations are isolated on the Azores and Canaries and on the larger Mediterranean islands. A second common European species, the Firecrest, is lighter green in body color and has a deeper-orange crown without the Goldcrest's yellow borders. The Firecrest breeds through most of continental Europe south to the Mediterranean islands and Asia Minor in mixed woodlands and deciduous scrubby growth. The little-known Formosan Kinglet, found only in the high mountain forests of Taiwan, closely resembles the Firecrest but has a brighter crown, a yellow rump patch, and black and white wing bars.

The kinglets are all active, unsuspicious birds that search tree needles and leaves for minute insects, eggs, and larvae, and pay little heed to humans close at hand. Outside the breeding season they travel in small scattered bands, often in company with the mixed flock of titmice, creepers, and woodpeckers that roam through the northern woodlands. When insect food is scarce, they eat small seeds and other vegetable matter. Their call notes are a thin "zee-zee-zee," so high-pitched it takes sharp ears to hear them. Their spring songs are pleasant little warbles, not very loud and, again, so high-pitched that, with one exception, you have to listen hard to hear them. The Ruby-crowned Kinglet is the exception—its song is surprisingly loud, highly varied and prolonged, sweet, fluent, and pure of tone. This may be compensation for the Ruby-crown's relatively small crown patch, which the female lacks entirely. Other kinglets display their brilliant crests to attract the opposite sex and to warn off rivals. The Ruby-crown seems to use music instead.

Kinglets build marvelous hanging purse nests of mosses, woven together with spider webs and thickly lined with bits of fur, feathers, and plant down. Both sexes work at building the nests, the female doing most of the construction. She incubates her large clutch of 7 to 12 tiny spotted eggs alone. The nest's interior is so small that the eggs are often deposited in two layers. The incubation period is long for such small eggs—usually from 14 to 17 days—and though both parents work hard to feed the young, it takes almost 3 weeks to fledge them.

If the 11 species of gnatcatchers and gnatwrens are correctly placed with the Old World warblers, they must be the descendants of sylviid ancestors that invaded the New World long ago, perhaps as early as Miocene time. The eight gnatcatchers of the genus *Polioptila* range from the northern United States southward through Central and South America to Argentina. One species is endemic to Cuba. The three gnatwrens (*Ramphocaenus* and *Microbates*) are found from southern Mexico to Brazil.

Typified by the Blue-gray Gnatcatcher of the United States and Mexico, the Polioptilinae are dainty, slender little birds, 4 to 5 inches long, with rather long, thin, pointed bills. All are dressed in soft grays, usually with some white on the rather long tail. Some species have black marks on the head. Extremely active, they strongly suggest tiny mockingbirds. Their long tails are continually in motion, bobbing up and down and from side to side as the birds work through the foliage in search of small insects.

Gnatcatchers forage through the outer leaves and twigs of trees, seldom on the trunks or main branches. Like the king-lets, they work the underparts of the leaves carefully, and when an insect takes flight will flutter after it and catch it on the wing. They also have the kinglet habit of hovering to pick the insects that can't be reached from the branch off a clump of leaves. Though the gnatcatcher's simple short "zee" call notes are easily heard, their songs are whispered rather than sung. The little birds have a varied repertoire of high-pitched trills and warblings. They also mimic the songs of other species, though always in a quiet monotone that one has to listen hard to hear. The gnatwrens inhabit the lower levels of the tropical forests and are usually encountered in pairs, hopping about through the vines of the understory with their long tails cocked up. Their song is a soft whistled trill on a single note.

Gnatcatchers build beautiful nests—compact little cups of plant down and flower petals bound together with spider webs and camouflaged on the outside with small bits of mosses and lichens. Usually the nest is saddled on a horizontal limb; sometimes it is placed within a forked branch. Gnatcatchers

**BLUE-GRAY
GNATCATCHER**
Polioptila caerulea
United States to Guatemala   5 in.

lay 4 to 5 pale bluish eggs finely spotted with brown. Both sexes incubate for the 13 days it takes the eggs to hatch. The young are fed entirely on insects by both parents, and one observer counted 43 feedings within 20 minutes. The young usually leave the nest 10 to 12 days after hatching.

The most aberrant of the sylviids are the 83 species of wren-warblers, the Malurinae of the East Indies, Australia, and New Zealand. Unlike the other three subfamilies, many

EMU WREN ♂
Stipiturus malachurus
Southern Australia
and Tasmania   7½ in.

VARIEGATED WREN ♂
Malurus lamberti
Southeastern Australia   5 in.

of these little birds are brightly colored in contrasting shiny blues, reds, blacks, and whites. They carry their long tails perpetually cocked up over the back in wren fashion, and most of them are commonly called wrens in the antipodes. Most are good singers, and a few are clever mimics. Active birds of the scrub and heath lands, the wren-warblers keep to the cover of the underbrush as they search industriously for small insects and larvae. They are usually encountered in small flocks, even in the breeding season.

Though a few of the wren-warblers build open cups, most of them make domed nests with entrances on the side or near the top for their 2 to 5 eggs. The nests are composed of plant fibers and grasses, often matted together with spider webs and other insect fibers and lined inside with plant down and feathers. The Variegated, or Purple-backed, Wren is typical of the group. One of the most curious is the tiny Emu Wren, whose tail is composed of 6 delicate feathers about 4 to 5 inches long, considerably longer than the body of the bird. The Emu Wren holds its tail upright as it works through the underbrush, and lets it stream out behind when it flies from bush to bush.

OLD WORLD FLYCATCHERS

PASSERIFORMES   MUSCICAPIDAE

Old World flycatchers live almost entirely on insects and catch them the same way the more primitive New World tyrant flycatchers do. Some have expanded their hunting methods to include gleaning insects from the foliage in warbler or vireo fashion. A few habitually pounce on insects on or near the ground. Unlike the thrushes and the warblers, with which they undoubtedly shared a common ancestor early in Tertiary time, Old World flycatchers have never successfully invaded the Western Hemisphere.

In physical equipment Old World flycatchers feature a comparatively broad, flat bill with a subterminal notch. They have well-developed rictal bristles about the nostrils which are a help in catching insects in flight. They are tree dwellers with little need for stout underpinning, their legs are rather short, and their feet are weak. They resemble the thrushes in that the young are usually spotted, but their tarsi are scaled, not smooth, in front.

Old World flycatchers vary greatly in color. Some groups are plain grays and browns, others are boldly patterned in black and white, still others sport brilliant blues, yellows, and reds. Some are crested; a few have bright facial wattles. In the duller-colored species the sexes tend to be alike; in many of the brighter ones sexual dimorphism is marked. While song is fairly well developed in a few species, the flycatchers are by no means the match musically of either the warblers or the thrushes. Most of them have rather harsh call notes, and their songs tend to be weak, monotonous, and repetitive, with very little individual variation.

Flycatchers' nesting habits are fairly uniform. Most of them build neat cups in the branches of trees or bushes using shredded leaves, mosses, and lichens, often tied together with spider webs. Some nest in holes in trees, under banks, or in clefts of rocky cliffs. Both sexes share all the nesting chores, but the female usually does most of the work. The flycatchers' 2 to 7 eggs may be white, greenish, or buffy in ground color and are often heavily spotted.

The muscicapids range throughout the Old World and have their greatest development in Africa and the Indo-Australian region. Most of the species that breed across Eurasia from the tree line southward are migratory. Members of the family have pushed eastward through the Pacific islands as far as the Marquesas and Hawaii. The some 378 species in the family are divided among four subfamilies, the largest and most widespread of which is the nominate subfamily Muscicapinae.

Among the commoner and less showy of these "typical" flycatchers are the Spotted Flycatcher of Europe and the similar Broad-billed Flycatcher of Asia. Somber gray birds about 5 inches in length, both are common summer residents in sparse woodlands, farms, suburbs, and parks. Their songs are undistinctive and somewhat unmelodious little warbles. The Spotted Flycatcher frequently nests around buildings. It builds a rather slight structure of moss and plant fibers tied together with cobwebs, sometimes on the deserted nest of another bird, often against a tree trunk. The sexes share the incubation (typical in most of the family), but the greater part of the burden falls on the female, whom the male feeds on the nest. Incubation takes 12 to 14 days, and the fledging period varies from 11 to 15 days.

One of the more brightly colored members of this subfamily is the Narcissus Flycatcher of eastern Asia, a flashy little black and yellow bird that summers in China, Korea, and Japan and migrates to the Philippines and the East Indies. Common in summer in deciduous forests up to 6,000 feet in the Japanese Alps, the Narcissus Flycatcher is one of the better singers of the family. It builds a nest of leaves, moss, and rootlets, usually on a branch well above the ground. It occasionally uses nesting boxes.

Another fine Asiatic singer is the Japanese Blue Flycatcher, a conspicuous summer bird in Japan that winters southward to Malaya. The male pours out his melodies from an open perch throughout the breeding season. The Japanese Blue Flycatcher builds a nest of mosses lined with rootlets, usually near the ground in crevices in rocky slopes or among exposed tree roots.

Africa, the wintering ground for many of the European and western Asiatic flycatchers, has perhaps a hundred resident species of its own. One of the most interesting is the Black-throated Wattle-eye, so named for the conspicuous red fleshy wattle above its upper eyelid. The wattle-eyes are representative of a group known as the puff-backed flycatchers. The members of this group raise and spread out their long rump feathers when excited. These restless birds flit conspicuously through the middle layers of the forest. They click their bills when catching insects as do their northern relatives, and also flick their wings audibly in flight.

The puff-backs build a typical flycatcher nest, a small cup of fine grasses and other fibers bound together with spider webs and camouflaged with lichens, usually in a forked branch. Like many small African passerines, these flycatchers are parasitized heavily by honeyguides and cuckoos, whose young soon grow to be twice the size of their foster parents. It is absurd, amusing, and pitiful to see a little flycatcher trying to brood and feed such an outsized incubus, whose demands for food must be enormous.

In Australia and from New Guinea to the Fiji Islands live a group of small muscicapids that the Australians call

JAPANESE BLUE FLYCATCHER ♂
Cyanoptila cyanomelana
Manchuria, Korea, Japan 5½ in.

robins. The five Australian robins of the genus *Petroica* are tame, friendly gray birds with red or pink markings on the breast and head. The Scarlet Robin and the Red-capped Robin live along roadsides and in dooryards and have cheerful trilling songs. Their anatomy, habits, and behavior, however, are those of the flycatchers, not of the thrushes.

Most striking of the flycatchers are the monarch and paradise flycatchers of the subfamily Monarchinae. Most of them are boldly patterned in blues, red-browns, or black and white. Many are crested, and in the paradise group the tails of the males are greatly lengthened. The sexes are unlike in this subfamily, and the usually unspotted young resemble the female. Their bills are broad, flat, and ridged, their wings rather long, their legs and feet small. These beautiful flycatchers are forest dwellers, and all are active, restless, and industrious. While they occasionally dash out to catch a passing insect on the wing, they hunt typically by scouring the foliage and smaller branches for their prey. They are usually solitary, but when not breeding may be found in small parties or accompanying the mixed flocks of other woodland birds that traipse through the forest in loose, scattered bands hunting insects.

The shorter-tailed monarchs, whose tails are only medium-long, range across southern Asia from India to the Philippines, south through the East Indies to Australia, and eastward in the South Pacific to the Solomons. One of the handsomest of the group is the Black-naped Blue Monarch. This widespread species, found from India to the Philippines and southward through Malaya, breaks into a number of distinct geographical populations over its wide range. Tamer and more friendly than others of the monarch group, its harsh call notes and rather pleasant trilling song are heard frequently from the trees in the native villages. It builds a deep cup nest of fine grasses coated with cobwebs, mosses, and lichens, usually in a forked branch at no great height. It lays from 2 to 4 pinkish-white eggs freckled with fine brown spots.

The exquisite long-tailed paradise flycatchers of the genus

1 BLACK PARADISE FLYCATCHER ♂
Terpsiphone atrocaudata
Japan, Ryukyus, Formosa 20 in.

2 PARADISE FLYCATCHER ♂
(white phase and red phase)
Terpsiphone paradisi
India to Manchuria,
Indochina, and East Indies 19 in.

3 BLACK-NAPED BLUE MONARCH ♂
Hypothymis azurea
India to the Philippines and East Indies 6 in.

4 SPOTTED FLYCATCHER
Muscicapa striata
Eurasia 5½ in.

5 NARCISSUS FLYCATCHER
Ficedula narcissina
Eastern Asia 5 in.

WILLIE WAGTAIL
Rhipidura leucophrys
Australia and New Guinea to the Solomons 8½ in.

GOLDEN WHISTLER ♂
Pachycephala pectoralis
Java and Australia to the Fiji Isls. 7 in.

Terpsiphone range from Africa through India, Malaya, the Philippines, and northward to China and Japan. The tropical forms are sedentary, the northern ones migratory. The male's long central tail feathers resembles those of the American Scissor-tailed and Fork-tailed flycatchers. In the New World species, however, the outer instead of the inner pair of feathers are elongated, and the birds acquire them in their first postjuvenile molt. The paradise flycatcher's longer central tail plumes do not attain their full 18- to 20-inch growth until the bird's third winter.

The Japanese Black Paradise Flycatchers reach Honshu in early May and establish their breeding territories in the mixed woodlands of the foothills. They are one of the most charming of the bird inhabitants of the extensive forests around the base of Mt. Fuji. Their striking cobalt-blue bill and wattled eyelids are as conspicuous in the field as the male's long tail, which streams behind him as he flies through the forest and does not seem to interfere in the least with his foraging. Nor does it prevent him from taking his regular stint at incubating. The paradise flycatchers build small but well-formed cup nests of thin grasses, moss, and bark tightly bound with spider webs and lined with thin rootlets. They lay 3 to 5 creamy eggs spotted with brown, and their 12- to 14-day incubation period is par for the family.

A third and well-marked subfamily of Old World flycatchers is made up of the fantails (Rhipidurinae), found from southeastern Asia southward to Australia and New Zealand and eastward on most of the South Pacific islands. The fantails all have long, rounded tails, which they keep moving constantly from side to side and up and down, spreading them in a fan and closing them again. They also droop their wings as they hop about. Restless, active birds of the forest undergrowth, the fantails are fond of brushy forest edges and clearings, and many are habitually found near water, along sea beaches and the banks of fresh lakes and streams. Tame and inquisitive, they make themselves at home around settlements. The sexes are similarly colored, usually in rather nondescript browns and grays, but the best-known members of the group are the conspicuously black and white birds typified by the Willie-wagtail of Australia.

The Willie-wagtail is a bird of the clearings. It followed the ax and the plow as Australia was settled to become one of the most familiar birds around farmsteads and suburbs. The constant companion of farm stock, the Willie-wagtail uses the backs and horns of cattle as a convenient perch from which to sally after the insects the grazing animals disturb. Strongly territorial, it defends its domain vigorously, and in kingbird fashion drives off species much larger than itself. Like all fantails, the Willie-wagtail builds a small, neat cup nest, usually low in a bush or a horizontal branch, and bound together so tightly with spider webs that it is extremely durable and hard to tear apart. Fantails' nests often have a tail of loose material.

The Pachycephalinae, or thick-heads (the fourth subfamily), are commonly known as the whistlers from their melodious flutey calls. Stocky-bodied birds with large rounded heads, the whistlers have rather heavy bills with a shrikelike hook at the tip. Most strongly developed in Australia and New Guinea, they range northward through Malaya and the Philippines and eastward through most of the South Pacific islands. Most of them are brownish to greenish gray above, lighter, often yellow, below. The throat is usually white, and the head and neck are variously patterned with black or yellow. Typical of the group is the Golden Whistler, found from the Malay Peninsula, Java, and Australia eastward to the Fiji Islands. This species breaks into some 80 or more subspecies over its wide range. In most populations the males are markedly brighter than the females; in some the sexes are alike. Their unspotted young resemble the female.

Whistlers are inhabitants of scrublands and the forest understory, where they search industriously for insects among the twigs and foliage. During the breeding season they are strongly territorial, and pairs call back and forth to one another antiphonally. When not breeding they may be found with loose flocks of other species wandering through the woodlands. They are active and curious, and can be whistled up by imitating their call. Whistlers build a fairly large and substantial cup nest near the ground which is the work of the female alone. The clutch is 2 to 3 eggs.

ACCENTORS

PASSERIFORMES   PRUNELLIDAE

Across Eurasia occur 12 species of small, inconspicuous, sparrowlike birds that are something of a puzzle to classify. Accentors look and act much like buntings, but they have thin, sharp-pointed, thrushlike bills, and rounded wings with 10 primaries. Rather robust little ground birds, quietly streaked and spotted in soft browns and grays, all but one of them, the Dunnock, are hardy inhabitants of high plateaus and mountaintops or tundra country above the tree line.

The 12 accentors are so similar to one another they are placed in the single genus *Prunella*. Their affinities are uncertain, but they seem most closely related to thrushes. The young are spotted, and they have moderately strong legs and feet, but their rather short tarsus is scaled, not booted as in thrushes. While they have melodious little warbling songs, their voices are neither as loud nor as outstanding as their common name suggests. In summer they eat quantities of insects, but in winter they subsist largely on berries and seeds. Like most seed eaters, they have a crop and a muscular gizzard, and they swallow grit to help their digestion.

Representative of the family is the widespread Alpine Accentor, resident in the Atlas Mountains of northwest Africa and from the Pyrenees and Alps of Europe eastward through the Himalayas to the highlands of Manchuria and Japan. While not uncommon, Alpine Accentors are extremely localized in their distribution, and eight geographical races are currently recognized. In summer they live well above the tree line. In winter they move to lower levels, usually in small, loose flocks. They are not shy, and will gather closely around mountain climbers to feed on crumbs from their lunches.

HEDGE SPARROW
Prunella modularis
Europe, Asia Minor   6 in.

ALPINE ACCENTOR
Prunella collaris
Mountains of Eurasia,
Spain to Japan   7 in.

They move over the ground with quick little hops or short darting runs. Their gait has a peculiar shuffling quality and they flick their wings and tails frequently as they run about.

Courting Alpine Accentors sing a warbling song from the top of a rock or a low bush, and the males make short, lark-like song flights. They build a neat cup nest of leaves, grasses, rootlets, and a few feathers in crevices in rocky screes, and lay 3 to 5 pale greenish-blue eggs, which both sexes incubate about 15 days. They feed their young at first on soft insects, later on seeds from their crop. The young sometimes leave the nest before they can fly, and may be attended by the parents for some time. Usually Alpine Accentors raise two broods each summer.

The Dunnock, often called the European Hedge Sparrow, lives at lower levels in scrub country and open moorlands, usually where there is some bush growth or shrubbery. It is also found along the European coasts and on rocky coastal islands where the winds and salt spray prevent forest growth. Though not particularly shy or uncommon, the Dunnock is rather quiet and unobtrusive, and remains close to the ground, usually in the shelter of hedges and shrubbery. It nests in hedges, in low evergreens, or in brush piles. In this species nest building and incubation are by the female alone. The male does not bring her food, and she leaves the nest regularly to forage. Incubation takes about 12 days, and the young remain in the nest another 12, being fed by both parents. The clutch is four eggs which, as throughout the family, are a clear blue-green, rarely with light spottings. The Dunnock starts nesting fairly early in spring, and customarily rears two broods each year, sometimes three. It migrates southward to the Mediterranean region in winter.

Two stray specimens of the Mountain Accentor collected in autumn on Nunivak and St. Lawrence islands off western Alaska admit it to the American list. Normally this Siberian species breeds from the Urals to the Chukotski Peninsula, in willow thickets along tundra streams. It migrates in winter to central Siberia, northern China, and Korea.

PIPITS AND WAGTAILS

PASSERIFORMES   MOTACILLIDAE

Trim, slender-bodied ground birds that walk and run rapidly but never hop, the pipits and wagtails have thin, pointed bills and live almost entirely on insects, which they capture on or near the ground. Essentially birds of open treeless country, most live in moors and prairies, arctic tundras, seacoasts or along streams and lakes.

WATER (ROCK) PIPIT
Anthus spinoletta
Northern Hemisphere 6½ in.

FOREST WAGTAIL
Dendronanthus indicus
Northern China,
Manchuria, Korea 5½ in.

YELLOW-THROATED LONGCLAW
Macronyx croceus
Africa south of the Saraha   8 in.

GRAY WAGTAIL
Motacilla cinerea
Eurasia   7 in.

PIED WAGTAIL
Motacilla alba
Eurasia, Iceland   7 in.

The 54 species in the family are divided among 3 genera of pipits and 2 of wagtails. The pipits, so called from their twittering voices, are a streaked and mottled brown. The sexes are alike or closely similar. The wagtails, which continually pump their long tails up and down, are more boldly patterned. The male wagtails are the more forcefully colored, and the juveniles often have a distinctive plumage. Both groups usually have the outer tail feathers white, or edged with white, which shows conspicuously in flight. They fly strongly with marked undulations, and call constantly on the wing. Most are migratory.

Pipits and wagtails have pointed wings and rather long, slender legs with partly scaled tarsi. An outstanding feature is their possession of 9 instead of the usual 10 primary wing feathers. Their structure and behavior suggest affinities to Old World warblers and thrushes. Their distribution points to an Eastern Hemisphere origin, and their fossils are found in upper Oligocene deposits 30 million or so years old.

The largest group in the family consists of the 34 very similar pipits of the genus *Anthus,* one of the most widely distributed of all passerine genera. Best developed in Eurasia and Africa, pipits occur practically throughout the world, but are absent from the Pacific islands. One species lives on South Georgia at the edge of the Antarctic. These pipits are all so alike they are very difficult to tell apart in the field. Plainly streaked little birds that match the colors of the dead grasses or bare ground that is their preferred background, their superficial resemblance to the larks both in appearance and habits is pronounced. Hence they are often called titlarks or fieldlarks.

Pipits migrate and winter in flocks and roost at night on the ground. They often forage in pastures among cattle for insects. Species that nest and winter along seacoasts hunt along beaches and around tide pools at ebb tide. Several pipits have the same tail-pumping habit as the wagtails, though it is usually less pronounced. One of these, the Tree Pipit of Eurasia, though essentially a ground bird, takes cover in trees and sings from a tree perch.

One of the most widespread species is the Water Pipit, or Rock Pipit, which nests in the arctic tundra the world around and winters southward. Another is Richard's Pipit, found from eastern Europe and Africa eastward to China, Australia, and New Zealand. Both these pipits are represented by many geographical races. Sprague's Pipit, a common American resident of northern praries, is famed for its spectacular courtship flight. Sprague's Pipit was discovered by Audubon, who named it for one of his field companions. Representative Eurasian forms include the Meadow Pipit, the Pechora Pipit, the Red-throated Pipit, and the Tawny Pipit, the subject of a most delightful English film some years ago. Africa has more than a score of pipits, some wintering, others resident such as the Plain-backed, the Striped, and the Short-tailed pipits.

Pipits build deep cup nests on the ground neatly woven of fine grasses and well hidden. Incubation is entirely by the female, but the male stands by and feeds her and the young. The eggs are usually white to buffy, heavily spotted with browns, and may number from 3 to 7. The incubation period in pipits runs from 12 to 16 days, and it takes the young another fortnight to fledge. Most are multibrooded.

One aberrant African group of pipits is fittingly called the longclaws. These eight species of the genus *Macronyx* have an exceedingly long hind toe and claw which facilitates their running over the tufted grasses of the veldt country. The hind toe of the common Yellow-throated Longclaw is almost 2 inches long, and the foot spans 3½ inches, almost half the bird's length. The longclaws have their upperparts cryptically colored for concealment, but most of them have brilliant yellow underparts crossed by a crescentic breast band. This gives them an astounding resemblance to the unrelated meadowlarks of North America.

Most of the 10 wagtails of the genus *Motacilla* live near water, along mountain streams and lake shores, and in swampy meadows or marshes. Wagtails are most plentiful in the temperate parts of Eurasia and Africa. Several species winter in southeastern Asia. The Pied Wagtail straggles occasionally to western Alaska, but only one species has successfully invaded the New World. The Yellow Wagtail breeds from Scotland across northern Alaska to Point Barrow and the northern Yukon. Alaskan wagtails migrate back to the Old World of their ancestors in winter, retracing their steps westward to Siberia, then southward.

Among the most unmistakable of Old World small birds are the several species of the widespread Pied Wagtails. Their contrasting black and white coloring is conspicuous. They are not at all shy, and they move about actively in the open. Pied Wagtails live across Eurasia and in Africa in a variety of habitats, always in open country and seldom far from water. Inland populations are found commonly in cultivated lands and around farms. Coastal Pied Wagtails are familiar in fishing villages, where they flit tamely along the shore and chase flies among the drying nets and lines.

The Yellow Wagtail and the very similar Gray Wagtail, both with gray-to-brown backs and yellow underparts, are a trifle wilder. They are commoner along streams and in swamps and meadows. One species, the Forest Wagtail of Eurasia, is a woodland inhabitant. Instead of constantly pumping its tail up and down as do all other wagtails, the Forest Wagtail swings its tail in a sidewise, somewhat circular motion.

When not breeding, wagtails are gregarious. Unlike the ground-roosting pipits, wagtails roost off the ground, in trees and bushes, or among marsh reeds. Migrating and wintering flocks sometimes roost together in thousands.

Wagtails are essentially ground nesters, and typically build a fragile nest of straw and rootlets lined with hair, feathers, and bits of paper. They may use nests of other birds in trees and bushes. Their eggs are colored like the pipits', and they lay a similar clutch of 4 to 7. In the wagtails, however, the male often assists in incubation. Like the pipits, wagtails are generally multibrooded. The northern migratory species usually rear two broods. The more sedentary tropical species space their nestings to coincide with the rainy seasons, when food is more plentiful.

WAXWINGS AND ALLIES

PASSERIFORMES   BOMBYCILLIDAE

This is something of a trash-basket family containing three small distinctive groups of birds each of which perhaps merits family rank by itself. Their affinities are obscure, but the three waxwings (Bombycillinae), four silky flycatchers (Ptilogonatinae), and the Hypocolius (Hypocoliinae) resemble one another more closely than they do the members of any other family. All are fruit-eating arboreal birds 6 to 9 inches long. All have somewhat broad bills, short legs, and 10 primaries. All have soft, silky plumage and are dressed in nicely blended drab colors. Their voices are poorly developed and none has an outstanding song. All are restricted to the Northern Hemisphere, and here their major similarities end.

Only the waxwings occur in both the Old and New worlds. The silky flycatchers are limited to Middle America, and the Hypocolius to southwestern Asia. Their spotty and restricted distributions, coupled with their lack of ties to other families, suggest all three to be relict groups that have persisted in their present ranges while their close relatives have vanished. Their kinship to one another is by no means certain, and grouping them in a single family, though convenient, may not express their true affinities. These await further clarification by more intensive study of their comparative anatomies and habits.

The three waxwings are so similar to one another they are placed in the single genus *Bombycilla*. They are sleek, strongly crested birds with smooth, velvety plumage, mostly fawn-brown in color, accented by a narrow band of bright yellow or red at the end of the tail. The sexes are alike, but immatures are duller colored than the adults. Their name refers to the small pellets of bright-red waxy material that form on the

BOHEMIAN WAXWING
Bombycilla garrulus
Eurasia, western North America   8 in.

tips of the adults' secondaries in the two best-known species. If these peculiar droplets serve any particular function it has yet to be discovered.

The 8-inch Bohemian Waxwing is the largest of the three species and the northernmost in distribution. It breeds irregularly in the evergreen and birch forests across northern Eurasia and in North America from Alaska south to Washington and Idaho. The slightly smaller Cedar Waxwing is similarly colored but lacks the Bohemian's white wing markings and has yellow instead of chestnut undertail coverts. The Cedar Waxwing nests throughout the woodlands of much of temperate North America and winters irregularly southward to northern South America. The Japanese Waxwing is similar to the Cedar, but lacks the wax droplets on the wings and has a red instead of yellow tail band. It breeds in the taiga forests of eastern Siberia and winters southward to Japan and Korea.

Waxwings are highly gregarious. They migrate and winter in close-knit flocks, and they stay together on the breeding grounds as well. Their flight is graceful, strong and fairly fast. Their migrating and wintering movements are nomadic. They show a marked lack of territorial fidelity, and their annual appearance in places where they winter commonly

PHAINOPEPLA ♂
Phainopepla nitens
Southwestern U.S. and Mexico   7 in.

HYPOCOLIUS
Hypocolius ampelinus
Arabia, Iraq,
Tigris-Euphrates Valley   7 in.

is never certain. At 4- to 7-year intervals large flocks of waxwings erupt southward far beyond their normal wintering range in both hemispheres into regions where they are seldom seen otherwise.

Waxwings are almost as irregular in their choice of breeding grounds, which they often shift from year to year. Their nomadism may be governed in part by the availability of their preferred foods. They consume a great variety of berries and small fruits, both wild and cultivated. Cherries are a favored item, as are the berries of cedars and junipers. Waxwing flocks seem to follow ripening fruit. In the spring and summer they eat flower petals in quantity, and are attracted by flowing sap. They also eat some insects, and feed them exclusively to their nestlings. Waxwings have short alimentary tracts for fruit-eating species and digest their food very rapidly, in from 20 to 40 minutes.

Waxwings are quiet, gentle birds, and usually are rather

tame. Their call notes are soft, thin, and lisping, and fairly high in pitch. Their songs in spring are faint, unimpressive warblings. They often nest fairly close to one another, each pair building a bulky cup-shaped nest of twigs and grasses lined with finer fibers, hair, and feathers, usually on an open branch with little attempt at concealment. Both sexes share the nesting duties, but incubation is principally, if not entirely, by the female, who is fed by the male. Waxwing eggs are an ashy gray spotted with brown and black. The clutch numbers 3 to 5; incubation takes 12 to 15 days, and fledging another 14 to 16. They are apparently single-brooded.

Best known of the silky flycatchers is the Phainopepla, a fairly common resident of the arid brush country of southwestern United States and Mexico. Three other species assigned to two different genera range from Mexico to western Panama. These birds resemble waxwings in their soft, silky plumage, in their prominent crests, and in their fruit-eating habits, but they eat more insects than other members of the family and catch them, flycatcher fashion, on the wing. They have shorter wings and longer tails than waxwings, and the sexes are dissimilar.

Silky flycatchers are somewhat gregarious and when not nesting usually travel in small flocks. They often sit on exposed perches with their crest raised. Like the waxwings their wanderings seem governed by the presence of berries. Mistletoe berries are a favorite food, and the birds doubtless help spread this semiparasitic plant. Their songs are short jumbles of short notes, on the weak side but nevertheless musical.

The Phainopepla is the only one of the subfamily whose nesting habits have been well studied. It builds an open cup-shaped nest in trees or bushes, much like that of the waxwings, but smaller. The male does most, if not all, of the nest building and performs a major share of the incubation. The breeding cycle is somewhat irregular, and the species is believed single-brooded. Clutches are small, usually 2 to 3, rarely 4, grayish-white eggs heavily speckled with brown and black. Incubation takes about 14 to 15 days.

Isolated in the Tigris-Euphrates Valley of Iraq but occasionally wandering to Arabia, Afghanistan, and western India and southward to the Persian Gulf is a strange crested bird the size of a Cedar Waxwing but largely bluish-gray in color and known only by its scientific name of *Hypocolius*. These birds travel about the scrub country in small flocks and live almost entirely on fruits, principally mulberries, dates, and figs. They fly strongly, and when they reach a tree or a bush, they fly directly into it instead of landing on an outer branch. They hide quietly within the foliage and are reported difficult to flush out. Like the other two subfamilies, they are rather quiet birds with low-pitched call notes and no noticeable song. Pairs nest by themselves, building a nest similar to those of the waxwings and silky flycatchers. They lay 4 or 5 milky-white eggs heavily spotted with brown at the larger end.

PALM CHAT

PASSERIFORMES　DULIDAE

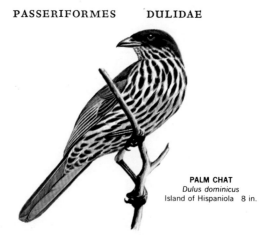

PALM CHAT
Dulus dominicus
Island of Hispaniola   8 in.

Restricted to the island of Hispaniola is the intriguing Palm Chat, which apparently became isolated there long, long ago. Though common and conspicuous on this rugged and heavily populated West Indian island, the species shows no close affinities to any other group of birds and is of uncertain ancestry and systematic position. It is difficult to say whether it developed its distinctive peculiarities in its insular isolation, or whether it has simply preserved there the characteristics of a formerly more widespread ancestor that has left no record of its existence elsewhere.

Of rather nondescript appearance, the Palm Chat's rather stiff, firm plumage is olive-brown above, yellowish-white below, broadly streaked with brown. The sexes are alike, and the immatures are darker and duller in color. The wings are of medium length and rounded, tail rather long, the legs and feet stout, the toes and claws long, and the rather heavy bill is laterally compressed and somewhat downcurved.

Noisily gregarious fruit eaters, the Palm Chats congregate in small flocks and utter their harsh, chattering notes in chorus. The birds live mostly on berries and flowers, are entirely arboreal, and never feed on the ground. One of their most striking attributes is their communal nesting. They build huge apartment-like twig structures the size of a bushel basket, usually placed conspicuously at the base of the fronds of a palm tree. Anywhere from 2 or 3 to as many as 20 or 30 pairs may combine to build the apartment. Each pair has its own separate compartment with its own private entrance from the outside and lined inside with soft bark and grass. The clutch is 2 to 4 white eggs heavily spotted with gray. After the breeding season the birds roost in these communal nests. Little else is known about their habits.

WOOD-SWALLOWS

PASSERIFORMES   ARTAMIDAE

The wood-swallows, small, plain-colored, aerial birds with chunky bodies and long, pointed wings, are most plentiful in Australia, where 6 of the 10 known species occur. The others range northward from India to the Philippines in southeastern Asia and eastward in the Pacific to the Fiji Islands. The name wood-swallow, which is applied to these birds in Australia and has become the accepted vernacular term for the family, is an unfortunate choice. In southeastern Asia, English-speaking people call them swallow-shrikes. While they feed almost entirely on insects caught largely on the wing and look something like stocky swallows in flight, the wood-swallows are in no way related to the swallow family.

The ancestry of wood-swallows can only be guessed at, for they show no close ties to any other living species. They show their nearest affinities, and these only vaguely, to the wax-wings and to the vanga-shrikes. Their plumage is soft and fine-textured, and their colors are drab browns, grays, or blacks relieved by a white rump or white underparts in some species. The sexes are alike or nearly so. Their bills are longish, stout, and slightly down-curved, and their gape is wide. Their short legs are stout and their feet are strong. Their necks are short. Their medium-length tails are square or slightly emarginate. The wood-swallows' outstanding peculiarity is their possession of powder downs, a specialized type of feather that grows continually and frays off at the end into a powder used for dressing the other feathers. Found in the tinamous, herons, parrots, and in the strange mesitae and cuckoo-rollers of Madagascar, powder downs are known to occur in no other passerine birds.

Some observers consider wood-swallows to be the most skillful and accomplished fliers among the passerines. They are the only perching birds, other than the Raven, able to glide for extended periods on motionless wings and to sail effortlessly into the sky on thermal updrafts. In flight they resemble stout-bodied swallows, but their flight is slower, more direct and less erratic, and marked by long stretches of soaring. Wood-swallows are usually seen in flocks hawking insects over forest clearings, grain fields, or rice paddies, often soaring high into the sky, almost out of sight. They keep up a harsh nasal twittering that can be heard from above when the birds are almost invisible.

Each flock usually centers its activities around some central vantage point, a high lone tree or a clump of tall waving palms or giant bamboos. There they perch quietly close together and sally forth individually to feed as the spirit moves them. Birds dash out fitfully from their perch after a passing insect and then spiral around in soaring circles a few moments before returning. They feed most actively in the early morning and late evening, and usually remain huddled quietly on their exposed roosts during the heat of the day. During plagues of locusts and other insects, wood-swallows flock to feed on the swarming pests and do yeoman service in controlling them. When flying insects are scarce, they will descend to the ground to feed on crawling insects and larvae. Rarely do they eat seeds, fruit, or other vegetable matter.

Throughout most of their range wood-swallows are common and quite conspicuous, for they are rather noisy and highly gregarious. They are often seen perched in long lines

WHITE-BROWED WOOD-SWALLOW
Artamus superciliosus
Australia 8½ in.

on telephone wires. At night they roost huddled together on high branches. During bad weather they take shelter in close-packed swarms under a leaning tree trunk, a projecting branch, or a loose flap of bark. They sometimes jam into narrow spaces one atop the other like a swarm of huge bees, always with their heads up.

Wood-swallows build frail, loosely constructed, saucer-shaped nests, usually on a branch. The 8½-inch White-browed Wood-swallow of Australia, one of the largest species, generally nests rather low down in a tree or bush. The Ashy Swallow-shrike of southeastern Asia usually nests 30 to 40 feet above the ground, and a favored site is the shelf formed by a projecting stub where palm leaves have broken away below the crown. The smallest member of the family, the 6-inch Little Wood-swallow of Australia, which looks in flight only half the size of its larger relatives, places its flimsy nest in tree cavities or in rock crevices on a cliff. The Little Wood-swallow often nests in colonies, as do some of the other species. So far as known, nesting duties are shared by both sexes in the wood-swallows. The eggs number 2 to 4; they are white to buffy in ground color, and are usually heavily spotted around the larger end, in which characteristic they strongly resemble the eggs of shrikes.

VANGA-SHRIKES

PASSERIFORMES   VANGIDAE

Isolated insular populations evolve so rapidly that nobody knows just when the vanga-shrikes' ancestors reached Madagascar; nor can we be sure just what those progenitors of the family looked like. As the less specialized vangas bear anatomical resemblances to the African helmet-shrikes (*Prionopinae*), it is probable that some primitive laniid crossed the Mozamibque Channel to found this isolated family of 13 distinct species assigned to 9 genera.

Most vangas are metallic black above, white below, or marked with chestnut or gray, and 5 to 12 inches long. Two have white heads, and the gayest of them is the Blue Vanga Shrike shown. Sexes are usually alike, females sometimes duller. Typically, vangas have stout, strongly hooked bills, but one species' is thin and down-curved, and another's bears a casque. Their wings are rounded, the tail usually short and square, the legs and feet short and stout.

All vangas are arboreal, occupying different niches in the forests. Most live in the treetops and search the foliage for insects, as do the Blue Vanga and the smaller Red-tailed Vanga, sometimes called the tit-shrike because it hangs upside down to poke under leaves and branches for its food.

The Rufous Vanga lives in the middle and lower forest strata, Lafresnaye's Vanga solitarily in arid brushlands. The Helmet Bird, which boasts a casque on its bill, flies rather heavily through the woodlands in small flocks. The Hook-billed Vanga, one of the more primitive species, ranges widely from the treetops to the ground, also in second-growth brushlands and mangroves. A solitary bird and deliberate in its movements, it sits motionless on a branch, turning its head slowly to watch for insects, small reptiles, and amphibians. Its call is a monotonous, long-drawn whistle. An aberrant vanga is the Coral-billed Nuthatch (*Hypositta*), which forages like a creeper, working spirally upward on tree trunks and the larger branches.

CORAL-BILLED NUTHATCH
Hypositta corallirostris
Madagascar 5½ in.

Most gregarious of the family is the thin-billed Sicklebill, which roves through the woods and savannas in flocks of 25 or more. The Sicklebill builds a large nest of twigs in a tall tree, but its nesting habits and behavior, like those of the rest of the vanga-shrike family, are practically unknown.

BLUE VANGA-SHRIKE
...opterus madagascarinus
Madagascar 6 in.

NORTHERN
(GREAT GRAY) SHRIKE
Lanius excubitor
Northern North America
and Eurasia 9½ in.

RED-BACKED
SHRIKE
Lanius collurio
Temperate Eurasia 7 in.

GORGEOUS (FOUR-COLORED)
BUSH-SHRIKE
Telophorus quadricolor
South Africa 8 in.

SHRIKES

PASSERIFORMES   LANIIDAE

Dashing and bold are the shrikes, the most truly predatory of the perching birds. They occupy somewhat the same position among the passerines that the hawks and owls do among the nonpasserines. Though shrikes are essentially insect eaters, many of them prey on small vertebrates—frogs, lizards, rodents, and even on birds almost as big as themselves. Unlike the hawks and owls, whose chief weapons are their strong talons, shrikes kill with their sharply hooked beaks. Their well-known habit of impaling their prey on thorns has earned them the common name "butcherbird."

Shrikes are small- to medium-sized birds, most of them 7 to 10 inches long, with large, broad heads and stout bills, strongly hooked and notched at the tip. Their shortish rounded wings have 10 primaries, and their tails are usually long and graduated. Their legs and feet are strong and their claws sharp. The more familiar Northern Hemisphere shrikes are plainly colored gray or brown above and white below, often with contrasting black or white markings on the head, wing, and tail. The black mask of the Northern and Loggerhead shrikes is duplicated in many Old World species. The sexes are generally alike, but are dissimilar in some species.

The shrike family is predominantly an Old World one, with its center of development and abundance in tropical Africa. As presently constituted it is divided into three subfamilies, the true shrikes (Laniinae), the bush shrikes (Malaconotinae), and the helmet shrikes (Prionopinae). The 39 bush shrikes and the 9 helmet shrikes are limited to Africa. The 25 true shrikes are widespread throughout Africa and Eurasia, but have never reached Australia or the Pacific islands south or east of the Philippines. Two species occur in the New World, the widespread circumpolar Northern Shrike, and the smaller Loggerhead Shrike. The Loggerhead, whose range extends to southern Mexico, is the family's only wholly nearctic species. Shrikes do not occur in Middle America or South America.

The shrikes' relationships to other families need further clarification, but with 72 of the family's 73 species of Eastern Hemisphere distribution, there is no question of their Old World origin. They are probably an offshoot from some primitive ancestor of the Old World flycatchers, the Muscicapidae. Their distinctness as a family points to their antiquity. Fossils of several living species are known from early Ice Age deposits, and of one, the Lesser Gray Shrike, from the Pliocene of Europe. The nominate genus *Lanius* is represented in early Miocene deposits in Hungary.

A well-known example of the true shrikes is the Northern Shrike, one of the largest species in the subfamily, which nests in the spruce forests completely across northern North America and Eurasia and winters irregularly southward when food is scarce in the north. In North America it divides into two geographical races, an eastern and a western, which merge clinally in the Hudson Bay region. Eurasia has a score of races, particularly along the southern edge of the species' range in southern Europe, northern Africa, and eastward to the Himalayas. More familiar to most Americans are the nine races of the Loggerhead Shrike, which nests widely across southern Canada and the United States. The Red-backed Shrike is an equally common Eurasian species that lives in temperate regions across the continent and migrates to Africa and southern Asia in winter.

Wherever they occur, shrikes are conspicuous birds, for they sit in a prominent open place with no attempt at concealment. Their actions are bold and aggressive. They fly strongly, usually undulating when traveling any distance, gliding shortly between wing strokes. They fly fairly close to the ground and sweep upward to their perch at the last moment. When hunting they may hover momentarily with fluttering wingbeats before striking, but usually they watch quietly from a commanding perch and pounce suddenly and directly when they spy their prey. If it is small and light, they carry it away in their beak; if it is heavier, in their feet.

The favorite food of most shrikes is large insects, such as grasshoppers, dragonflies, locusts, and crickets. These they hold in their feet and tear apart with their beaks. Their curious habit of impaling their prey on thorns (barbed wire is a frequent substitute in cattle and farming country) may have developed from the difficulty of holding tougher animals in their feet while tearing them apart. Originally the thorn may have served them as a butcher's hook to give them better purchase for dismembering their catch, and they left the remains after eating their fill.

Like many predators, shrikes often kill more than they can eat, and when opportunity presents itself seem to kill for the joy of killing. Bird banders have to watch their traps carefully when there are shrikes in the vicinity, for a wandering shrike that happens into a trap full of birds will kill every bird fluttering within reach before starting to eat. Shrikes usually have a favorite larder within their territory where they hang their catch. It is not uncommon to find a thorn tree or barbed-wire fence decorated with a dozen or more grasshoppers, locusts, mice, or small birds.

That the shrikes establish such larders in times of plenty against future need has been questioned. They often fail to return, and the carcasses slowly shrivel or rot. Studies on several species show individual birds do remember where they have cached their food. A Japanese ornithologist counted 68 such caches made by one Bull-headed Shrike within its territory during the autumn. The bird returned and gradually consumed its stores during January and February, when live prey was scarce.

Seldom are predators of any sort gregarious, for each individual needs quite a bit of territory to forage over. Shrikes are no exceptions, and throughout most of the year they are encountered singly at intervals over the countryside. While most of the north temperate zone species are migratory to some extent, mass movements are seldom observed in these solitary birds. The migratory instinct is not highly developed, and varies in intensity and regularity. Some may remain near the breeding grounds all year, while others move irregularly southward in winter. Their wanderings seem determined more by food supply than by season. Every two or three winters an influx of Northern Shrikes invades the northern United States; at other times almost none appear.

The Northern Shrike preys more on small birds and mammals than do most other shrikes, particularly in winter when insects are scarce in the north. Its dashing attacks on titmice, sparrows, and other small birds have not made it popular with tender-hearted bird lovers, who fail to realize that the fierce predator is a useful biological regulator of lesser species and is an essential part of the natural scheme of things. Back in the latter part of the 19th century, shortly after the European House Sparrow was introduced to this country, Northern Shrikes became so numerous on Boston Common one winter that men were hired to shoot them to protect the sparrows. Little did our forefathers realize that the House Sparrow would soon become far too plentiful for man himself, much less for shrikes, to control.

Shrikes start pairing off in late winter as the springtime breeding season approaches. They build bulky, loose, deep cup nests of twigs in a shrub or tree from 5 to 20 feet above the ground. The Northern Shrike lines its nest heavily with grasses, feathers and hair, for it lays very early in spring and, like most shrikes, rears at least two broods each year. Clutches vary from 3 to 6, and the eggs are typically a dirty white or tinted bluish to pinkish in ground color, always heavily spotted with grays or browns about the larger end. Incubation among the shrikes is almost exclusively by the female. Though the male may take short stints on the eggs, he usually spends his time bringing food to the incubating female. The incubation period is 14 to 16 days, and the young leave the nest 2 to 3 weeks after hatching.

During the breeding season shrikes are rather quiet and go about their business inconspicuously. When nesting is over and the pairs break up and scatter out on their own, shrikes become fairly vocal and announce themselves with unmelodious cries and rattles. The name shrike derives from the same root as shriek, and refers to their shrill calls. They have a wide range of vocal expression, and some species imitate the calls of other birds skillfully. Shrikes are sensitive to the weather and sing but little when it is overcast and wet. They are noisiest on fine, dry days.

The large subfamily of African bush shrikes is divided among seven genera, which vary considerably in appearance. Most of them are much more brightly colored than the laniine shrikes, and the sexes are generally unlike. Despite their brilliant colors, they are hard to observe, for they are shy birds of dense thickets and heavy cover. They skulk in the underbrush and hunt on or near the ground. They feed mainly on insects, but many of them are predatory on frogs, lizards, snakes, and mice. Some are notorious nest robbers, taking both the eggs and nestlings of other species. Representative of the bush shrikes are the Gorgeous Bush Shrike and the Black-headed Gonolek.

Most bush shrikes have loud, melodious voices and reveal their presence by distinctive calls. Many of them sing antiphonally, the male piping one phrase, the female answering immediately with another. Bush shrikes build a loose open cup nest in branches fairly near the ground. Their clutches are smaller than those of the true shrikes, two eggs being the usual number, occasionally three. Both sexes build the nest, but incubation is almost entirely by the female, and takes about 12 days. The young are ready to leave about 15 days after hatching.

The helmet shrikes are such a distinctive group that they are sometimes given full family rank. They are boldly patterned, usually black above and white or buffy below. Their stiff forehead feathers project forward over the nostrils, and their eyes are surrounded by a conspicuous wattle. Residents of wooded and forested Africa south of the Sahara, helmet shrikes are markedly gregarious and, as might be expected, are not as predaceous as other shrikes. They live almost entirely on insects, hunting for them like so many large warblers or titmice. They move through the treetops in noisy

STRAIGHT-CRESTED HELMET SHRIKE
Prionops plumata
South-central Africa   8¼ in.

bands of 5 to 20 birds, chattering continually to one another and snapping their bills audibly. This curious bill snapping is typical of the entire subfamily.

Helmet shrikes even remain together in small groups when breeding, and in the Spectacled Crested Shrike three or more individuals may share in the nest building and the feeding of the young at a single nest. Helmet shrikes build a cup nest of grasses and twigs in a tree fork 15 feet or higher above the ground, and lay 3 to 4 eggs, usually pale-blue spotted with brown. They are reported to be pugnacious in defense of their nests, and to attack large animals and even humans who approach too closely.

STARLINGS

PASSERIFORMES   STURNIDAE

Thanks to man's misguided assistance, the sometimes too-familiar Common Starling has become the most widely distributed member of this family of aggressive Old World birds. During the past century man has helped it across the oceans and other natural barriers that originally confined it to the western palearctic region. Its range is now almost cosmopolitan. South America is the only major land mass on which it has not as yet gained an impregnable foothold.

The 111 species in the starling family are of Old World origin and distribution, with their centers of greatest development in the Ethiopian and oriental regions. All but three of them are grouped in the nominate subfamily Sturninae, which in turn is apportioned among some 26 genera. They are a fairly well-defined group and, though their ancestry is uncertain, starlings most probably arose from primitive thrush-like stock. One of the earliest passerine fossils known is considered intermediate between the starlings and the thrushes. The fossilized impression of the skeleton of this early perching bird, named *Laurillardia,* was found in France in Eocene deposits about 50 million years old.

As a group, starlings are jaunty, active birds of medium size with straight or slightly down-curved bills. They have strong, stout legs and feet, and while a few hop occasionally, most of them walk cockily with a waddling gait. Their flight is strong and direct, and their pointed wings have 10 primaries, the outermost one greatly shortened. Typically the tail is short and square, though it is rounded in some and long and pointed in a few.

Starlings are generally dark-colored, most of them black with metallic sheens; some are brown or gray, others brightly marked with white, yellow, or, less often, red. Many are crested, and a number sport prominent wattles or bare patches of skin on the head. The sexes may be alike or unlike. The immatures of most species differ from the adults in having a duller plumage often streaked or scaled, which is probably indicative of the ancestral adult type.

Starlings molt but once a year, immediately after breeding. The seasonal variation in their plumage, which is often marked, is accomplished entirely by feather wear. The name starling, meaning little star (some of the smaller gayer species are now called starlets), comes from the spangled appearance of the Common Starling in its fresh autumn plumage. The buffy star-spots at the tips of the fresh feathers wear away gradually during the winter, leaving the bird a shining glossy black by spring. The bill also changes color in the Common Starling, its horny brown of fall and winter becoming a bright ivory-yellow as the gonads enlarge and the birds come into breeding condition in the spring.

While starlings probably originated as forest birds, only a few groups live in deep woodlands. Most of them prefer open, broken country. The most successful species have associated themselves with man and are most abundant in cultivated regions. Their basic diet is insects and fruit, but those that live near man are catholic in their food selection, and take a varied diet including birds' eggs and garbage.

Many starlings are insectivores. The Common Starling consumes great quantities of noxious insects. The Gray Starling, which replaces the Common in eastern Asia, is one of the few birds that feed extensively on the rice stem-borer, and for this reason is protected in Japan. The Rosy Pastor of

AMETHYST STARLING
Cinnyricinclus leucogaster
Tropical Africa   7 in.

HILL MYNA
Gracula religiosa
India to Indochina and Malaya   13 in.

GOLDEN-CRESTED MYNA
Mino coronatus
Burma, Thailand,
Indochina   8 in.

southeastern Europe and southwestern Asia follows the cyclic swarms of locusts, and nests whenever and wherever these periodic pests become plentiful.

Another famous nomadic locust eater is the Wattled Starling of South Africa, where it is widely protected. The Wattled Starling is unique in that the males, and occasionally the females, shed their head feathers and grow conspicuous wattles during the breeding season. This species also has no regular breeding season or place, but nests periodically and colonially when stimulated by a superabundance of food. When the locusts swarm, flocks of Wattled Starlings gather to the feast from miles around.

Most starlings are gregarious, some of them highly so. The temperate zone species are migratory, and usually travel and winter in flocks, sometimes of tremendous size. They often gather in spectacular numbers to roost at night. Just before going to roost, and again at dawn, the flocks climb high into the air and execute a series of mass evolutions. Wheeling and turning in unison with almost military precision, the birds course back and forth in tremendous twittering swarms before settling down for the night or scattering for the day's foraging.

Starlings are generally noisy and garrulous, and chatter to one another continually in flight and when roosting. The Common Starling has a large vocabulary of creaking, grating, wheezing, rattling notes that it intersperses with clear musical whistles. It sings in the fall as well as in spring, and sometimes sings at night in its winter roosts. Many of its notes are too high in pitch to be heard by the human ear, with frequencies above 8,000 vibrations per second. Starlings often incorporate imitations of other birds in their songs, and several rank high as mimics.

Among the best of all talking cage birds are the Asiatic mynas of the genus *Gracula* that range from India and Ceylon through the oriental region. The Hill Myna, commonly called a grackle in India, is a large, glossy black starling with yellow head wattles. Isolated populations vary considerably in size, from 12 to 15 inches. Hill Mynas travel through the forests in small noisy flocks and live largely on fruits. In the wild their notes vary from low, hoarse chuckles to loud, ringing whistles that carry far. In captivity their imitations of human speech are far superior to those of any parrot. I have heard several tame mynas with astonishingly extensive vocabularies, and with an enunciation so perfect that there was not the slightest doubt of what they were saying.

The Common Myna (*Acridotheres*) of southern Asia is a stocky, 10-inch brown and black bird with white wing patches, a short crest, and naked patches of orange skin about the eyes. A noisy, vigorous species that prefers open country and feeds much on the ground, it is not as attractive a cage bird as the Hill Myna and does not learn to talk as well. It has been introduced successfully in almost as many parts of the world as the Common Starling. Similar in appearance to the Hill Mynas are three species of Papuan Mynas (*Mino*), found from New Guinea eastward on many of the Southwest Pacific islands. Commonest of the Pacific island species are the 20-odd glossy starlings (*Aplonis*), most of which are black with metallic sheens, and are regarded as one of the more primitive groups of the family. In appearance and

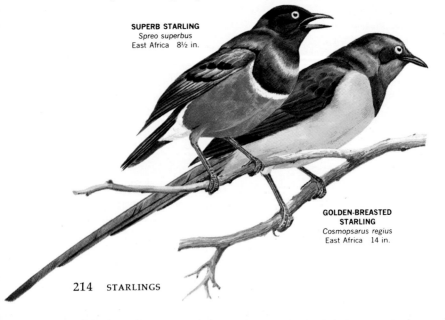

SUPERB STARLING
Spreo superbus
East Africa   8½ in.

**GOLDEN-BREASTED
STARLING**
Cosmopsarus regius
East Africa   14 in.

COMMON STARLING
Sturnus vulgaris
Europe, western Asia   8½ in.

ROSY PASTOR
Sturnus roseus
Southeastern Europe,
southwestern Asia   8½ in.

behavior the glossy starlings I encountered in the South Pacific reminded me strongly of American blackbirds.

The Sturninae are well developed in Africa, where a large complex of 16 dark, shiny species with tails of varying lengths is assigned to the genus *Lamprotornis*. Among the more striking of the African forms is the Golden-breasted Starling, a slender-bodied bird whose sleek grace is accentuated by its long, tapering tail. The Golden-breasted Starling feeds largely on termites, opening their ground tunnels with rapid flicks of its bill, and catching the insects skillfully on the wing when they take flight. The Superb Starling is representative of 10 brightly colored African species of the genus *Spreo* which live on both insects and fruit. This species feeds on the ground in small flocks, and is rather tame and congenial. It builds a round domed nest of thorny twigs lined with feathers, usually in a bush or low tree.

Nesting habits vary considerably in the starling family,

but in most of those that have been studied the pair bond is strong and both sexes share the various nesting duties. Starling eggs are usually a clear blue-green; they are white in a few species. In several genera, *Aplonis, Gracula,* and *Mino* among them, the eggs are spotted with brown. Clutch size varies from 2 to 9, but is usually 3 to 5. Most starlings are cavity nesters and build in holes in trees, either natural ones, or holes abandoned by, or usurped from, woodpeckers. Some nest in cliff or wall niches, others under embankments. Those that have associated themselves with mankind, such as the Common Starling, use sites in buildings, behind shutters, under eaves, or on any projecting ledge. They are expert at finding their way into belfries, towers, and attics.

One of the South Pacific glossy starlings (*A. metallica*) builds a large woven hanging nest in the treetops, much like that of a weaverfinch. When a hatch of locusts encourages the African Wattled Starling to breed, the birds nest colonially. They build massive covered nests of sticks and twigs, usually within the protection of thorny trees or shrubs. Often several pairs mass their nests together, 2 or 3 touching one another. Sometimes a dozen or more of these double or triple nests occupy the same thorn tree.

The Rosy Pastor is another colonial and opportunistic breeder. It nests in huge crowded colonies when conditions are right, starting suddenly and finishing its breeding cycle in a hurry. Each pair builds a crude, untidy nest, heaping twigs or grasses together in crevices in rock hillsides, cliffs, walls, or ruins. The Rosy Pastor lays 5 to 6 pale bluish eggs, which are incubated by the female alone. The incubation period is short, usually 11 to 12 days, and the young, fed by both parents, leave the nest in 14 to 19 days after hatching. This irruptive breeding behavior is doubtless conditioned by and adapted to the transitory nature of the insect swarms that trigger it into action. The Rosy Pastor rears but a single brood, and as soon as the young are securely on the wing the birds quickly wander away in search of fresher and richer feeding grounds.

The Common Starling sometimes nests in small colonies, but more often singly. Like the Rosy Pastor, it makes a loose, bulky open pad of sticks and straws for a nest in any convenient cavity. The normal clutch is 4 to 5 clear-blue eggs, which both parents incubate for 12 to 14 days. The young remain in the nest almost 3 weeks and fledge fully before leaving. This helps reduce the usual high juvenile mortality rate. The Common Starling is multibrooded, and pairs use the same nest for 2, sometimes 3, successive broods. The nest soon becomes fouled by the droppings of the young, for nest sanitation, practiced by most passerines, is distinctly not a starling trait.

The Common Starling's success in establishing itself when carried by man to corners of the globe far from its natal habitat bespeaks its adaptability and aggressiveness. It is one of four vertebrates, the others being the House Sparrow, brown rat, and house mouse, all originally inhabitants of Europe, which man has spread widely over the planet, purposely for the two birds, accidentally for the two mammals. Most dramatic and best documented of these cases has been the introduction and subsequent spread of the Common Starling in North America during the past half century. This outstanding example of the dangers latent in foreign introductions was largely responsible for the present federal laws controlling the importation and release of wild birds in the United States.

A dozen or more attempts were made to introduce starlings in various parts of the United States and Canada between 1870 and 1900. All failed except one—the 60 birds released in New York's Central Park in 1890, followed by 40 more in 1891. These started to breed at once, and the first nest was found under the eaves of the American Museum of Natural History adjoining the park in the summer of 1890. From these 100 birds have descended the millions of starlings that now occupy most of settled North America.

For the first few years the Central Park starlings remained in New York. As their numbers increased they began to wander, particularly in the fall and winter. By 1900 they had reached New Haven, Connecticut, and Bayonne, New Jersey. In another 10 years they had appeared in most of New England and in the Middle Atlantic states. Their expansion followed a set pattern. The birds invaded new territory during their winter wanderings. Where they found conditions suitable, a few remained to breed instead of returning to their natal area. These remained static until the local population built up, and shortly their descendants moved on to fresh conquests. By the early 1930's starlings had expanded throughout the Middle West, northward into southern Canada, and southward into northern Florida. The first ones crossed the Rockies into California in the 1940's.

Starlings were introduced with the best motives in the world—in Europe they are cheerful and useful bird neighbors that consume great quantities of harmful insects. But by the time they had gained an impregnable foothold in North America and had begun to appear in large flocks in the suburban countryside, it was realized, too late, that their presence had undesirable elements. Though their extensive insect consumption is on the positive side, their inroads on crops of grains and small fruits are considerable. Starlings compete for wild fruits with native thrushes and waxwings, and for nesting sites with highly valued hole nesters, such as bluebirds and woodpeckers, whose numbers decline wherever starlings take over.

The starlings' worst habit has been their flocking into cities in tremendous hordes to roost in winter. In this respect, they have become a prime nuisance. The situation became acute in Washington, D.C., during the early 1930's. Wintering flocks that fed by day over the surrounding countryside streamed into the heart of the city from every quadrant late in the afternoon. The birds lined the ledges on the government buildings, swarmed into the trees on Pennsylvania Avenue, and perched in noisy windrows in every nook and cranny in the foyers of theaters and department stores. Their droppings soiled the buildings, and the streets and pedestrians below them as well. In residential districts their night-long wheezing and chattering kept people awake. In the past two decades other eastern and midwestern cities have been subjected to similar starling plagues. A famous roost is on the girders supporting the Hudson River Parkway viaduct in New York City. Birds stream in every winter evening from the New Jersey and Long Island marshes.

Control of the starling nuisance in cities is a serious civic problem that has yet to be solved satisfactorily. Trapping, netting, poisoning, and shooting have not reduced the birds' numbers effectively. Efforts to drive them away with flares, firehoses, smudgepots, noisemakers of all sorts including electronic magnifications of their alarm notes, and most recently by painting their roosts with sticky pastes, have afforded only temporary relief. Architects are now designing buildings to eliminate all ledges where the birds might roost.

Fortunately the starling problem now shows signs of abating by itself. The first great population explosion seems ended in the eastern states. In places the huge wintering flocks are gradually diminishing, and the birds are settling down into a more static biological niche. Starlings have now established regular migration patterns in North America, largely in a northeast-southwest direction paralleling the movements of their European forebears.

The Common Starling has been introduced to South Africa, Australia, New Zealand, and Jamaica with roughly similar consequences. In each case the newcomers remained quiescent until they gained strength in numbers. Then they suddenly expanded explosively, with unfortunate effects on native birds, on crops, and on human peace. The species has also increased and expanded in its European home during the past century. It has followed human cultivation northward into northern Scandinavia and the subarctic islands. Starlings reached Iceland in the 1930's, and have been breeding there regularly since 1941.

The Common Myna, as mentioned above, has also been introduced widely around the world in the past century. It has gained strong footholds in South Africa, Hawaii, New Zealand, Australia, and on many islands in the Pacific, Indian, and South Atlantic oceans. About 1900 the related Crested Myna was introduced to Vancouver, British Columbia. It became well established there, but fortunately has not as yet been able to expand as the starlings have done elsewhere. The British Columbia population is believed to number about 20,000 Mynas today, and seems to be remaining steady. Just what the ecological conditions are that allow it to prosper in this one area around Vancouver without spreading are unknown. Wildlife management experts still have their fingers crossed against Mynas crossing the barrier of biological intolerance that apparently keeps them from establishing a population in more favorable territory to the south. Straggling Mynas have been reported in Oregon and Washington. A Myna plague could be disastrous in the California fruit country.

Despite the rampant success of these adaptable starlings, the family contains several species that became so specialized in limited environments that they vanished when civilization reached them. One such species was a small starling that lived with the Dodo on Rodriguez and Reunion islands in the Indian Ocean. Some 23 specimens of it are known, the last taken in 1840. A handsome, glossy black starling (*Aplonis*) that once lived in the forests of Kusaie Island in the eastern Carolines is known only from a few skins in the Leningrad Museum. It is thought to have been exterminated by rats that came ashore on Kusaie from whaling ships in the 19th century. Rats from a ship wrecked on tiny Lord Howe Island in the Tasman Sea between Australia and New Zealand in 1918 quickly wiped out another glossy starling there.

Two aberrant African starlings, the Red-billed and Yellow-billed oxpeckers, form the subfamily Buphaginae. These strange starlings have adopted a life with, and actually upon, large animals. Their food consists mainly of the ticks they pull from the animals' hides, and they also sip the blood that oozes from tick wounds. Oxpeckers have broadly thickened beaks; their legs are short, their claws sharp and curved, their tails stiff and pointed. They climb about on all sorts of large wild animals and domestic cattle as a woodpecker climbs tree trunks. The animals seem to pay little attention to the birds unless they get too close to their eyes or noses.

Africans regard oxpeckers with mixed feelings. Hunters dislike them because they warn their animal hosts of danger by flying up with rattling cries. Game photographers love them because of the interest they lend to pictures of big game. Bushmen and primitive farmers value them for ridding their cattle of ticks. Commercial cattlemen are against them because they claim the birds keep tick wounds open in order to drink the blood. However, oxpeckers waste no time on tick-free animals, and soon disappear from ranges where the cattle are dipped regularly and there is no big game about for them to feed from.

Oxpeckers are cavity nesters. The Yellow-billed nests in holes in tall trees. The Red-billed breeds commonly under the eaves of buildings, in the thatched roofs of native huts,

YELLOW-BILLED OXPECKER
Buphagus africanus
Africa south of the Sahara 8½ in.

in rock cavities, or along embankments. Each builds an untidy nest of grass or straw lined with animal hair, and lays from 3 to 5 white to pale-blue eggs variously spotted with brown in it.

Placed tentatively with the starlings as a third subfamily, the Pityriasinae, is the rare and little-studied Bristle-head of Southern Borneo forests. Although it had long been classified with the helmet shrikes because of its peculiar head feathering, and sometimes placed in a family by itself, what little is known of the Bristle-head's behavior and habits has led most students today to regard it as a highly aberrant starling.

HONEYEATERS

PASSERIFORMES   MELIPHAGIDAE

The 162 species of honeyeaters form one of the dominant and most characteristic families of Australia, New Zealand, and the islands of the Southwest Pacific. Most are rather small birds, only a few exceeding thrush or jay size. Many are drably colored in greenish browns, grays, and yellows; others are boldly patterned with blacks, whites, and reds. They live in the forests and brushlands, and feed, as their name implies, mainly on flower nectar and small insects. All have slender, down-curved, pointed bills, and a long extensible tongue with a brushy tip and sides that curls around to form a tube for sucking nectar from forest flowers. All have 10 primaries and rather long pointed wings. The tail may be short or quite long; the legs are normally shortish and strong.

The family has its greatest development in Australia, where more than half the known species occur, and is well represented from the Moluccas eastward through the Papuan region and the South Pacific islands. One branch of the family reached Hawaii, where 5 or 6 forms were once found on as many of the islands. These were the birds the Ha-

O-O (extinct)
Moho nobilis
Hawaii   13 in.

waiians called the *O-o* and whose yellow feathers they used for the unique capes of their royalty. The O-os lived in the mountain forests and disappeared rapidly when the native woodlands were destroyed. While it is hoped that the O-o (*Moho bracatus*) may still exist on Kauai, the others are

NOISY FRIARBIRD
Philemon corniculatus
Eastern Australia   12 in.

TUI
Prosthemadera novaeseelandiae
New Zealand   11 in.

certainly extinct, for none has been recorded since early in the 20th century. Persecution by native Hawaiians for their feathers has commonly been blamed for the disappearance of these birds, but destruction of their forest habitat as the island plantations were developed by Westerners is the more likely cause of their extinction.

The Helmeted Honeyeater is typical of a large complex of Australian honeyeaters, most of which are olive-greenish in color, with tufts of yellow feathers around the head or neck. These honeyeaters of the nominate genus *Meliphaga* are essentially inhabitants of vast eucalyptus forests, though some species prefer oak growth or acacias. A number are common visitors to gardens and city parks when the trees come into bloom. Quite a few antipodean flowering trees are ornithophilous, i.e., dependent on birds for cross-fertilization. Their flowers are shaped to facilitate pollination by honeyeaters and other nectar-sipping birds.

The Helmeted Honeyeater and its relatives travel through the forests in small bands and feed together among the flowers of a tree in bloom. Active, aggressive birds, they quarrel among themselves while feeding and jockey for positions next to favorite flowers. They stop bickering when a bird of another species appears and join forces to drive it away from their feeding site. All honeyeaters build open cup-shaped nests in trees or bushes composed of small twigs and lined with plant down or animal hair. One species, the White-eared Honeyeater, is so tame during the nesting season it sometimes lights on people's heads to steal hair for nest-lining material. Most lay 2 or 3 eggs, which may be white or tinted with markings of darker shades.

Another large group of honeyeaters is formed by the many *Myzomelas*, bright-colored little birds 4 to 6 inches in length found widely throughout the Pacific islands. In most of these the sexes differ in color, the males being brilliant blacks and reds, the females dull greenish. Dichromatism varies greatly within the genus. In some species the males are dull-colored like the females; in a very few the females

CARDINAL HONEYEATER ♂
Myzomela cardinalis
Micronesia, Samoa, Solomons,
New Hebrides   4½ in.

HELMETED HONEYEATER
Meliphaga cassidix
Southeastern Australia   8 in.

have a bright plumage similar to that of the male. Except when they settle down to rear their broods, *Myzomelas* are nomadic, wandering about in small flocks in search of flowering trees and shrubs. Their nesting habits are typical of those of most of the family in that they build an open cup-shaped nest and lay 2 to 3 eggs. The female does most

CAPE SUGARBIRD
Promerops cafer
South Africa   17 in.

of the nest building, but the male may do some of the incubating, and always helps feed and rear the young. Incubation in these little birds is fairly lengthy, reported as about 18 days, and the nestling period is equally long.

The friarbirds and wattlebirds of Australia are honeyeaters that have bare spaces or wattles about the head. These jay-sized birds are among the larger honeyeaters, and most are gray in color. Many are highly vocal. The Noisy Friarbird, whose unattractive naked head of black skin is responsible for its vernacular name of "leatherhead," has raucous calls. It wanders about cultivated lands and settlements and is reported occasionally to damage orchards. Wattlebirds, so called because of the yellow or red wattles behind the eye, likewise eat fruit as well as nectar and insects. Their nomadism has reached the point of seasonal regularity, so that in southern Australia they are classed as migrants. At one time they were hunted for their flesh, which is excellent eating, and because they are large enough for shooting, and travel about in flocks. They are now protected throughout most of Australia.

Song is highly developed in most honeyeaters, and one of the best performers is the Tui, which New Zealanders consider among the finest of their forest songsters. The Tui's song is loud, varied, musical, and pleasant, and the bird is a competent mimic as well, imitating the songs of the other birds it hears and such unbirdlike sounds as the squealing of a pig, a boy whistling to his dog, and even the dog's barking. The Tui's two white patches of curly feathers at the throat, like the collars worn by 19th-century divines, led New Zealand settlers to call it the "parson bird." Though not as plentiful as it was before the original bush was cut, the Tui is still fairly common in New Zealand, for it has been able to adapt itself to man's occupancy of its habitat far better than have two other New Zealand members of the family, the Bellbird and the Stitchbird.

The New Zealand Bellbird, whose notes in chorus sound like the chiming of little silvery bells, is still to be found in some of the few patches of original forest now remaining, and is reportedly fairly common in some of the forest reserves. Bellbirds are about 9 inches in length, the male dark green in color, the female browner. They are shy and are heard more often than seen. Both sexes sing equally well.

The little 7-inch Stitchbird, whose notes sound like two pebbles struck together, was last reported limited to a very small population on little Barrier Island off the coast of North Island. The male Stitchbird is velvety black above with prominent white feather tufts on the sides of the head and bands of yellow across the breast and at the bend of the wing. The female is a dull brown with a few whitish feathers on the sides of the head and a small white mark in the wing. The few Stitchbird nests that have been described were in holes in trees, a most unusual site for a member of this family. The nest is made of small sticks and rootlets, and is lined with feathers and tree fern scales. The clutch is five pure white, glossy eggs.

Stitchbirds feed entirely on nectar, and even feed their young on it exclusively. This may be partly responsible for their failure to withstand the radical changes in their environment brought on by civilization. The native Maoris used the yellow feathers from the breast of the Stitchbird for ornamental cloaks the same way the Hawaiians did those of the O-o. The introduction of rats and other predators has also affected the Stitchbird and the Bellbird adversely. There seems little question, however, that here again change of habitat rather than human persecution has been responsible for the disappearance of the bird.

Placed tentatively with the Meliphagidae in the subfamily Promeropinae are the two odd South African sugarbirds, found only from Southern Rhodesia southward. They may not be correctly placed here, for it is difficult to see how honeyeater stock could have reached South Africa from Australia without leaving representatives in southern Asia, the Indian Ocean islands, or elsewhere in Africa. Sugarbirds resemble the honeyeaters strongly in structure and habits. They have the same type of tongue and live largely on nectar, mainly from the flowers of trees of the genus *Proteus*. They also eat insects. Despite their similarities to the honeyeaters, which are the only group of birds they resemble closely, they could have developed from an entirely different stock by the process of convergent evolution.

The male Cape Sugarbird is the largest of the meliphagids; with its long tail, it measures 16 to 17 inches in length. The female is as large-bodied, but is only 11 inches long. Sugarbirds build open cup nests, lined with plant down, usually in a bush. They lay two buffy, blotched eggs.

SUNBIRDS

PASSERIFORMES   NECTARINIIDAE

Old World sunbirds invariably invite comparison with the American hummingbirds. Though the two groups are in no way related, the sunbirds are in many ways the counterparts of the hummingbirds, which they rival in diversity of brilliant colors though not of form. While the sunbirds' flight is strong and fast, they are no match for the hummers in flying skill. They feed similarly on nectar and small insects, but prefer to sit down to their meals, perching on or beside the flower they are working on. They can—and occasionally do—feed on the wing, scanning leaves for insects or hovering before blossoms they can't reach otherwise. They sip nectar from small flowers through the open throat, as hummingbirds do, but large flowers and those with long tubular corollas they pierce at the base with their long pointed bills.

The sunbirds show their closest affinities to the honey-eaters and the flowerpeckers, but they are a compact, well-marked group, well differentiated from their two nearest relatives. In structure they resemble the honeyeaters most closely, particularly in the shape of the bill, which is narrow and down-curved but longer, and has fine serrations on the cutting edges near the tip. The sunbird's tongue, however, is quite different. Its outer two-thirds is a double tube that opens into a trough leading back to the esophagus, and its tip, instead of being brush-tipped, is divided into 2 forks, in some groups, 3. The sunbirds' 10-primaried wings are shorter and more rounded than those of the honeyeaters, and their legs are usually shorter.

The 104 species of sunbirds are all tiny, most of them less than 6 inches long. A few have elongated central tail feathers that add an inch or two to their length. Strong sexual dimorphism is the rule in the family, and the bright hues are limited to the males. The females are usually dull gray, brown, or olive-green above and lighter below, and

REGAL SUNBIRD ♂
Cinnyris regius
Congo and Uganda   5 in.

GOLDEN-WINGED SUNBIRD ♂
Nectarinia reichenowi
East Africa   4 in.

SCARLET-CHESTED ♂
SUNBIRD
Chalcomitris senegalensis
Central Africa   6 in.

PURPLE SUNBIRD♂
Cinnyris asiatica
India to Indochina 4 in.

VARIABLE SUNBIRD♂
Cinnyris venustus
East Africa 4½ in.

**LITTLE
SPIDERHUNTER**
Arachnothera longirostris
India to the Philippines
and East Indies 6 in.

are often barred, streaked, or spotted. Immature sunbirds resemble the female, but in a few species the young males assume full breeding dress directly.

The sunbird family is widespread through the warmer forested portions of the Old World and has its greatest development in tropical Africa, where more than half the known species live. Sunbirds also range across southern Asia from Israel eastward, and more than a score of species inhabit Malaya. Only one species reaches northern Australia, but several extend out into the Pacific islands. Sunbirds are usually resident wherever they occur. They may move about during the nonbreeding season, shifting their feeding grounds as various trees and plants come into bloom, but they show no clear migration patterns.

Though sunbirds often gather together to feed when some favored tree or patch of flowers comes into bloom, they are not innately gregarious. Some are pugnacious and defend feeding grounds as well as nesting territories against intruders. Their voices are poorly developed, and their thin, metallic calls do not carry far. Courting males utter a twittering, chattering excuse for a song.

An outstanding sunbird characteristic is the hanging, purselike nests they build of plant fibers woven and matted together or bound with spider webs. The nest is usually hung from a branch fairly near the ground, seldom more than 10 feet up, and little attempt is made to conceal it. A few species make neat, compact bags, but most sunbirds' nests are ragged. The bottom is extended with loose trails of fibers with a leaf or two tangled in, so that they are easily overlooked as bits of accumulated rubbish. The nest is lined with plant down, fur, or feathers, and the entrance is on one side near the top and usually covered by a portico.

Though the pair bond is strong and pairs seem to remain together throughout the year, the nesting chores devolve largely on the female sunbird, in some species entirely so. The division of labor is by no means constant within the family and needs further study, but incubation is apparently done by the female alone. In some species, as in the White-breasted Sunbird, the male occasionally helps with nest building and brings food for the young. Sunbird eggs are generally white or buffy and heavily blotched. The usual clutch is 2, rarely 3, and in those species that nest several times yearly, only one. Incubation is reported as 13 to 14 days, and the fledging period another 17 days.

Centered in the oriental region are the nine species of spiderhunters, all of the genus *Arachnothera,* which are such a distinct and uniform group they are sometimes given subfamily rank. The spiderhunters lack the bright metallic hues of the rest of the family, and the sexes are usually dressed alike in gray-browns, dull yellows, or olive-greens. From 6 to 8½ inches in length, they have longer, stronger bills and feed to a greater extent on insects. The Little Spiderhunter of Indochina feeds extensively on the nectar of banana blossoms and probes deep into the flower tubes as it clings to the purple bracts, often upside down.

Most spiderhunters build a unique cup-shaped nest attached to the bottom side of a broad leaf. They sew the rim of the cup to the leaf with cobwebs or vegetable fibers, knotting the strands on the upper side. The leaf forms the roof of the nest, and the entrance is a semicircular hole in the side of the felted cup. Both sexes share the duties of nest building, incubating, and rearing of the young. The eggs are normally 2, though occasionally 3 are reported.

FLOWERPECKERS

PASSERIFORMES   DICAEIDAE

The smallest birds one sees commonly in the oriental and Australian regions are the flowerpeckers. Most of these active, chunky little bundles of feathers are barely 3 inches long, and only a few exceed 6 inches from the tip of their bills to the end of their short, stubby tails. The 54 species in the family are divided among 6 genera. The largest, commonest, and most typical group is formed by the 33 species of the genus *Dicaeum*. These are to be found throughout the range of the family, from India to Formosa and the Philippines, southward to Australia, and eastward in the Pacific to the Solomons.

The family is most diversified in the Papuan region, where it is believed to have arisen. The flowerpeckers probably share a common ancestor with the sunbirds, which seem to be their nearest relatives. They have a similar long tubular tongue and fine serrations on the edges of the terminal third of their bills. Flowerpeckers' bills vary somewhat in shape, but are never as long and thin as in the sunbirds. Typically they are shorter, thicker, and slightly down-curved. An important family characteristic is the reduction in length of the outermost primary. This is strongly manifest in the primitive forms, and in the more advanced and typical genera such as *Dicaeum,* the 10th primary is vestigial. Flowerpeckers lack the bare spots or wattles on the head that characterize many honeyeaters and sunbirds, and only one species shows a crest.

Color patterns vary throughout the flowerpeckers, but generally the birds are dressed in solid hues, and only a few are streaked below. Usually the sexes are strongly unlike, though they are similar in a few species. The males have dark backs, often with a glossy sheen, though this is seldom metallic. Most are lighter, and sometimes white below. Many sport bright patches of red or yellow on the head, back, rump, or breast. The females are usually a duller, plain dark olive-brown above and lighter below. Where the sexes are similar, the colors are usually not bright. In one Philippine group the females are closely similar to the bright males.

True to their names, flowerpeckers spend some of their time pecking around flowers for small insects, and some groups feed extensively on nectar, but the mainstay of most species, especially the dicaeids, is small fruits and berries. A favorite food is the small sticky berries of the tropical mistletoes (*Loranthus*), so much so that one of the common Australian species is called the Mistletoe Bird. Flowerpeckers are roundly blamed for spreading these epiphytes, which are often a scourge on mango trees.

Flowerpeckers spend much of their time in treetops, but frequently descend closer to the ground when low-growing shrubs come into flower or, later, into fruit. Though they are occasionally found in mixed groups with other species attracted to the same food, flowerpeckers are generally not gregarious. In the Solomons I found the Midget Flowerpecker, singly or in pairs, flitting through shrubs at the edges of forest clearings and around the native villages, never in the heavy forests. Their call notes are short, somewhat metallic chirps, often repeated at some length. Some species are reported to have a simple warbling song as well, but the family is by no means noted for its vocal abilities.

Most flowerpeckers build nests like those of the sunbirds, small, deep purses hung from a branch and woven of plant down and other fibers strengthened with cobwebs into a feltlike consistency. The nest of the Mistletoe Bird is pear-shaped with a slitlike opening near the top. Some species reinforce the entrance by weaving tougher grasses around its edges, and others protect it with a small hood woven of the same materials. Nest building and incubation in the typical flowerpeckers are entirely by the female, though the male often accompanies his mate for nest material. He also helps feed the young.

So different from the typical flowerpeckers as perhaps to deserve subfamily rank of its own is the group of seven chubby little diamondbirds found in Australia and Tasmania. They are sometimes called pardalotes, from their generic name *Pardalotus,* which means leopardlike and refers to their bright spotting. Diamondbirds are similar in size and proportions to the flowerpeckers, but have shorter, deeper bills which are notched behind the tip and are not serrated. They live almost entirely on small insects and insect larvae. They forage for these like titmice, scouring the bark, leaves, and twigs. They are usually encountered in pairs working the outer branches of large forest trees, usually fairly high up.

Diamondbirds differ greatly from flowerpeckers in their breeding habits. While they build a similarly domed nest,

MISTLETOE BIRD ♂
Dicaeum hirundinaceum
Australia   3¾ in.

YELLOW-TAILED DIAMONDBIRD ♂
Pardalotus punctatus
Southeastern Australia   3¼ in.

they make it largely of strips of bark and grasses, and place it in a cavity. Most of them dig a tunnel 1½ to 2 feet into the earth and build at the end of it. The Yellow-tailed Diamondbird digs down into level or slightly sloping ground; the Spotted Diamondbird burrows into a bank or into the soil around an uprooted tree. The Red-tipped Diamondbird uses the natural holes in trees, and occasionally nests in crevices in buildings, as do several other pardalotes. Both sexes cooperate in digging the tunnels and in building the bulky nest; and the male takes his turn regularly at incubating. The eggs vary from 3 to 5 according to species, and are pure white without markings.

WHITE-EYES

PASSERIFORMES   ZOSTEROPIDAE

The most uniform of the larger passerine families are the small yellowish-green birds called white-eyes from the narrow ring of white feathers around their eyes. With the preceding three families, the white-eyes complete the complex of Old World nectar-eaters. They show their closest affinities to the honeyeaters, for their tongues are brush-tipped instead of tubular as in the sunbirds and flowerpeckers. They are considered the most advanced of the four families because their 10th primary is at best vestigial and usually absent.

White-eyes are very much alike. They are from 4 to 5½ inches long, and their colors range from olive-green to grayish-brown above and from yellow to gray or white below. Their only conspicuous feature is the eye ring, which varies somewhat in width, is partly complete in a few forms, but is rarely absent. The Yellow-spectacled Zosterops of the Lesser Sunda Islands is the only species in which the eye ring is not white. White-eyes' bills vary slightly in length and thickness, but are typically rather slender, pointed, and slightly

ORIENTAL WHITE-EYE
Zosterops palpebrosa
India to Philippines   4 in.

down-curved. Their wings are generally rounded, their square tails of medium length, and their legs short but strong.

Such slight differences separate the many distinct populations of white-eyes that the group is both the delight and the despair of avian systematists. Very similar forms often occupy different habitats side by side, and apparently never intermingle. The latest revision recognizes 85 species divided among 12 genera. As the differences between these genera are less marked than those between species in other families, some conservative workers lump almost all white-eyes into the nominate genus *Zosterops*.

White-eyes range throughout Africa south of the Sahara, across southern Asia from Arabia to the Pacific, north to China and Japan, and south to Australia and New Zealand. They have pushed eastward in the Pacific to the Carolines, Fiji, and Samoa. Carried by man to Hawaii within the past century, they have spread from island to island. White-eyes seem to be expanding their ranges. The Common White-eye of Australia appeared suddenly in New Zealand in the early 1850's and now occupies most of the outlying islets too. One hardy group settled that antarctic outpost, Macquarie Island.

The family's success in reaching and colonizing oceanic islands is remarkable. White-eyes are not particularly strong fliers and, except for a few populations of high altitudes or latitudes that retreat to warmer climes in cold weather, they are not migratory. Their marked success at island hopping apparently stems from their gregariousness. Except when breeding, white-eyes move about in flocks, sometimes of hundreds of birds of both sexes. Hence the chances of enough pairs reaching distant islands to colonize successfully when carried there by the vagaries of wind and weather are far better than in less gregarious species.

Arboreal birds that eat insects and some fruits and berries, most white-eyes also feed on nectar, a few of them almost exclusively so. They obtain nectar both by poking down into the center of the flower and by pecking holes through the base of large blossoms. White-eyes also work over leaves and outer branches for small insects. During the breeding season the males have a tinkling, warbling song.

As so often where the sexes are alike, the nesting chores in the white-eyes are divided, with the male assuming his fair share. Breeding patterns show little variation in the widely separated species that have been studied in Africa, India, Australia, and Japan. Each pair selects its territory and builds a dainty open cup nest of vegetable fibers bound with spider webs and lined with hair or rootlets. The nest is usually fastened between the tines of a horizontal fork in a low tree or bush. The clutch varies from 2 to 4 eggs, which range from unmarked dark blue to blue-white. The incubation period is 11 to 12 days; the nestling stage usually takes another 9 to 13 days.

VIREOS

PASSERIFORMES   VIREONIDAE

In our lineal sequence the vireos are the first of six families that represent the peak of evolutionary development among New World oscines. These six families contain slightly more than 800 species, almost a tenth of the world's birds. All are distinguished by having only nine functional primaries.

Whether they stem from a single or, more likely, from several parent stocks is uncertain, as are their affinities to other passerine families. Members of only two families, the Hawaiian honeycreepers and the New World seedeaters, have expanded beyond the American continental limits. All are unquestionably of Western Hemisphere origin.

Each of these six families forms a fairly discrete unit, but the dividing lines among them are not always clear. Opinions differ on their systematic relationships, and the placement of a few intermediate genera is still somewhat arbitrary. Several shifts in family groupings and realignments of the lineal sequences have been proposed. Researchers now being conducted in their comparative anatomies, in their breeding behavior, and in related fields are certain to result in further refinements in the classification of these birds. Full family rank may prove warranted for several groups treated here as subfamilies.

Vireos are the most sharply differentiated of the six families, and are considered the most primitive because many of them retain a vestigial 10th primary feather. In this respect they parallel the Old World flowerpeckers, but their Eastern Hemisphere counterparts are the white-eyes. Like the white-eyes, the vireos are rather undistinctive small birds, 4 to 6 inches long, the sexes dressed alike in plain olive-greens and gray-browns. Their habits are somewhat similar, and they build the same type of nest. These resemblances are the result of convergent evolution, and the two groups are not related. Anatomically and distributively, the vireos' closest living relatives seem to be the wood warblers, from which they differ mainly in their thicker, heavier bills, slightly hooked and with a small notch or tooth near the tip.

The 42 species that form the family are divided into three subfamilies. The vireos and greenlets (Vireoninae) contain 37 species spread widely throughout the forested parts of the Americas from central Canada south to Argentina. The 3 shrikevireos (Vireolaniinae) and 2 peppershrikes (Cyclarhinae) range from southern Mexico to central South

America. The family's distribution is thus centered in the tropics from Central America to northern South America. As practically all the temperate zone breeders in this family, both north and south, migrate to the American tropics to spend their winters, this was doubtless their ancestral home.

The vireos are among the few well-known birds whose scientific name has become widely accepted as their common name. The only other English name ever used for these birds was the term greenlet, often applied to vireos in the 19th century, but now commonly restricted to members of the tropical genus *Hylophilus*.

Vireos inhabit the outer foliage of trees and shrubs and hop about very deliberately among the branches, searching for small insects. In the fall and winter they supplement their insect diet with seeds and berries. They are partial to the fruits of the elderberry, huckleberry, pokeberry, and magnolia among others. Highly valued as insect destroyers, vireos are notable as the most persistent avian singers. One of the most indefatigable is the Red-eyed Vireo, whose prattling, rather colorless monologues led early New Englanders to dub it "the preacher."

Through the spring and summer the Red-eyed Vireo almost never stops singing from dawn to dusk. It sings in series of short but pleasantly musical phrases of 2 to 5 notes. Each individual bird varies its phrases, and may use a score or more modulations of the theme. Phrases often end on an upward inflection, as though the bird were asking a question, which it answers in the next with a downward strophe, then punctuates momentarily as it grabs an insect before asking the next one. A persevering Canadian ornithologist spent a day counting the songs uttered by a single bird. The grand total was 22,197. Even in Ontario, where the June days are 20 hours long, this is more than 1,000 songs per hour!

The Red-eyed Vireo is one of the 20 species of the genus *Vireo*, and the most widely distributed member of the family. Representative forms of it range from Canada to southern Brazil and Argentina; some 12 geographical races, which differ very little from one another, are recognized. The northern and the southern populations spend their respective winters in the Amazon jungles, which are occupied by resident subspecies that do not migrate.

Eleven other *Vireo* species nest in North America. All are similar to the Red-eyed in general appearance and behavior, but are individually recognizable by slight differences in color and pattern when you can glimpse the singer hidden among the leaves. Some have conspicuous wingbars, eye rings, eye stripes, or other features that are responsible for their names —the White-eyed, Black-capped, Yellowthroated, Yellow-green, and Blueheaded vireos. Vireos are more easily recognized in the field by their characteristic songs, which vary so between species that the good field observer soon learns to differentiate among them.

One of the easiest songs to recognize is that of the White-eyed Vireo. It consists of loud, short-phrased warbles inter-

RED-EYED VIREO
Vireo olivaceus
Southern Canada to Argentina   6 in.

YELLOW-THROATED VIREO
Vireo flavifrons
Eastern North America   5½ in.

spersed with clear whistles and catlike mews, each phrase typically beginning or ending with a short "chick." Found throughout the central and eastern United States southward through the West Indies (where several subspecies are resident) and through Mexico to Nicaragua, the White-eyed Vireo is smaller than the Red-eyed and has whitish wingbars in addition to its conspicuously white eye. It is a bird of thickets and shrubbery, partial to brushlands, and a frequent summer resident in suburban gardens. Active, inquisitive, and almost as noisy as the Red-eyed, it is easy to lure into sight by squeaking.

The 15 species of greenlets of the genus *Hylophilus* are tropical vireos found from Mexico to Brazil. They are all similar grayish-green birds that differ from the *Vireo* group mainly in having a somewhat longer, more slender bill. They are a maddeningly nondescript genus, and lack the prominent wingbars and head markings that make vireos fairly easy to tell apart in the field. Their habits are essentially those

CHESTNUT-SIDED SHRIKEVIREO
Vireolanius melitophrys
Mexico and Guatemala   7 in.

GRAY-HEADED GREENLET
Hylophilus decurtatus
Mexico to Panama   4 in.

RUFOUS-BROWED PEPPERSHRIKE
Cyclarhis gujanensis
Mexico to Argentina   6½ in.

of the nominate group. They live in scrub and tree growth and forage through the foliage for insects with the same deliberate movements. All are persistent singers of the same sort of loud, short-phrased songs.

An outstanding vireonine characteristic is their type of nest, a neat open cup of grasses and insect fibers invariably slung between the horizontal arms of a forked branch. Most vireos build near the ground, from 2 to 10 feet up in a leafy tree or shrub, though some tree inhabitants, such as the Red-eyed, Yellowthroated, and Philadelphia vireos, occasionally build much higher. Nest building in the vireos is almost entirely by the female, but as in most groups where the sexes are alike, with few exceptions the males assist with the incubation. The males' periods of incubating and brooding average shorter than the females', but they take a more active part in feeding the young.

Vireo eggs are white lightly speckled with brown. The clutch varies from 3 to 5, and the eggs are laid a day apart, usually early in the morning. Vireos start incubating when the first egg is laid, and the young hatch a day apart, 13 to 15 days later. It takes them another 10 to 14 days to fledge. The northern vireos have but one brood a season, but those in warmer regions may raise two. Vireos are exceptionally tame at the nest. Many allow a close approach before flushing, and then stay near the intruder, scolding and trying to drive him off. So strong is the habit of singing that in most vireos the males invariably, and the females often, continue to sing while incubating.

Peppershrikes and shrikevireos are each frequently given separate family rank, but both are so close to the vireos in behavior and anatomy this hardly seems warranted. Slightly larger than the typical vireos, the two peppershrikes have much heavier and more strongly hooked bills. They inhabit bushlands and the forest edges around tropical clearings, and are usually found fairly near the ground, moving through the foliage in deliberate vireo fashion. They eat large insects, which they hold down with their feet and tear apart with their beaks, and also some fruit and berries. Their flight is rather weak, but their voices are loud. They have harsh scolding notes and a musical warbling song that is given as persistently as in the vireos. Peppershrikes build a rather fragile nest hung in a forked branch and lay 2 to 3 pinkish-white eggs blotched and speckled with brown.

The three shrikevireos have not been well studied and their nesting habits have not been described. The Chestnut-sided Shrikevireo of southern Mexico and Guatemala is a bird of the treetops and lives largely on fruits, supplemented with some insects. It is the most strikingly marked of the family, and has the same type of loud, persistent song.

HAWAIIAN HONEYCREEPERS

PASSERIFORMES   DREPANIDIDAE

Paleobotanists tell us that the first forests capable of supporting arboreal birds probably developed in Hawaii in mid-
Pliocene time about 5 million years ago. The ancestors of
the Hawaiian honeycreepers probably arrived soon thereafter. They prospered and diversified so rapidly that it hardly
seems possible for such variations to have developed from a
single ancestral type in so short a time. Hawaiian honeycreepers provide a dramatic example of adaptive divergence,
and are a living (and disappearing) proof that evolution
works fastest in small, isolated populations, where random
heritable changes have the best chance of surviving.

The 22 highly varied species in this purely Hawaiian
family are indeed an oddly assorted group. They are from
4½ to 9 inches long, and their colors range from plain
greens and grays to bright yellows, reds, and black, but are
never metallic or glossy. Most remarkable is the great variation in the size and shape of their bills, doubtless in response
to the availability of particular types of foods. Some drepa-
nidid bills became long, thin, and down-curved for probing
flowers for nectar and insects. Others became the short, heavy
seed-crushers of a grosbeak or a parrot. One species that
probes into bark for insects has a straight bill like that of a
woodpecker. The Akepa, now rare, has tips of the mandibles
crossed uniquely sidewise, perhaps to help it open leafbuds.

Recent anatomical studies have shown that despite these
divergencies, the Hawaiian honeycreepers are probably descended from a single ancestral stock. Their progenitor was
most likely a nectar-sipping insect eater with a relatively
unspecialized bill and tongue. As the group shows its closest
affinities to the New World nine-primaried oscines, it is now
thought that some long-vanished members of this great com-

plex (perhaps tanagers) managed to cross 2,000 miles of ocean from the American mainland to found the dynasty.

The Drepanididae are divided into two subfamilies, representing two main lines of development. The more primitive Drepanidinae, the thick-skinned honeycreepers, are mainly red and black; the sexes are similar, with the male somewhat larger. Their head feathers are stiff and pointed, and their sharp-edged primaries produce a whirring sound in flight. They wander through the forest in small, loose flocks, visiting various flowers as they come into bloom, extracting the nectar by piercing a hole in the base. Some also eat soft-bodied insects. A member of this group was the Mamo, a species the Hawaiians used for their feather cloaks. The Mamo has not been taken since 1892, and was last reported alive in 1898. Four other species the Hawaiians used for cloaks still exist, and two of them, the red Iiwi and the Apapane are fairly common.

The second subfamily, the Psittirostrinae, has mostly greenish plumage. The sexes differ in this group, the males often showing bright yellow or orange. The head feathers are soft and fluffy. The green honeycreepers are insect, seed, and fruit eaters, and probably represent a later evolutionary expansion. They are more sedentary than the Drepaniinae, and strongly territorial. The males have a courtship song, which is lacking in the thick-skinned group. The commonest of the surviving honeycreepers, the Amakihi, is one of this group. It occurs on all the larger islands.

Drepanidids breed from January to July, making rather simple open cup nests in trees or shrubs, some in the grass. The eggs are white, usually spotted, and number 2 to 4. Incubation is by the female, but both parents tend the young.

Hawaiian honeycreepers demonstrate dramatically that rapid evolution and ultraspecialization usually mean a short species life. Of the 22 species of drepandiids known, 9 are extinct. Another 8 or 10 survive precariously in small, local populations. Several species formerly widespread over all the islands now occur on only one or two. Of 39 known

HAWAIIAN HONEYCREEPER ♂
Vestiaria coccinea
Hawaii 6 in.

forms, 24 (more than 60 per cent) are now extinct or nearly so. The three commonest species are the least specialized.

The seed and fruit eaters were apparently the most specialized forms and the first to disappear. Two seed eaters of the genus *Psittirostra* have not been reported since the 1890's. Rarest in collections is a pretty little gray and red bird which the Hawaiians called the Ula-ai-hawane (*Ciridops anna*). It is known from only five specimens, all from the island of Hawaii, the last taken in 1892.

The fiction still persists that the Hawaiian honeycreepers were exterminated by Hawaiians who killed the birds to use the feathers for chieftains' cloaks. Their decline actually dates from the arrival of Americans, and its basic cause was the inability of ultraspecialized forms to adapt themselves to the environmental changes initiated by the newcomers. Destruction of the original forests, introduced predators, and little-known bird diseases also played a large part in wiping out so many of the Hawaiian honeycreepers.

WOOD WARBLERS AND BANANAQUITS

PASSERIFORMES   PARULIDAE

Perhaps no group of birds gives the growing coterie of American bird watchers more all-around enjoyment than the wood warblers. No one the least bit interested in birds can fail to be thrilled by a morning afield in spring when a real warbler flight is going through. This always occurs at that delightful time when the trees are just budding. The woods that were barren of birds yesterday are suddenly alive with scores of bright-colored little warblers of a dozen or more easily identified species in full breeding dress. Yet one of the greatest challenges offered the amateur is to identify these same birds in the fall, when they have molted into maddeningly similar drab plumages with few distinguishing marks, and those hard to discern.

Americans refer to this family simply as the warblers, a term too ingrained to be changed, yet an unfortunate choice. First, very few of the family can be said to warble in the true sense of the word, which Webster defines as "singing in a trilling manner, softly and quaveringly with rapid modulations in pitch." Second, the term implies a nonexistent relationship to the Old World warblers (Sylviidae). To prevent confusion the New World family is more accurately called the wood warblers.

The Parulidae are a fairly compact group of New World nine-primaried oscines. Their relationships to the other groups in this complex are uncertain, but anatomically they seem closest to certain tanagers and emberizine finches. The family now has about 119 species, but may have less if a few birds are reduced to subspecific rank. It is divided into two subfamilies—the 109 insect-eating warblers (Parulinae), widely spread throughout the Americas, and the 10 nectar-eating bananaquits and conebills (Coerebinae) of the West Indies, Central America, and South America. Until recently the latter were classified in a separate family (the honey-creepers, Coerebidae) with 30 other nectar eaters now placed with the tanagers.

Wood warblers are small, dainty birds with slender, pointed bills and rounded tails. All have rictal bristles, often inconspicuous, and best developed in the redstarts and other species that capture insects on the wing. Most warblers glean small insects among the leaves and twigs—each species in its preferred niche: some in the treetops, others in low shrubbery, a few on the ground. Many species also eat small berries and seeds in the fall and winter.

Wood warblers range from somber grays and olive-browns to bright yellows, blues, and reds, but yellow is the commonest bright color in the family. In most of the 59 migrant species that nest in North America and winter southward, the males are more brightly patterned than the females, especially in spring. In the tropical groups the sexes tend to be alike, even in the brightly colored ones, such as the Painted Redstart and the Red Warbler of Mexico.

A peculiar trait of the warblers is their tendency to produce occasional hybrids between species. Crosses between the Blue-winged and Golden-winged warblers, both members of the genus *Vermivora,* produce the fairly well known Brewster's Warbler and the less familiar, recessive Lawrence's

COLLARED REDSTART
Myioborus torquatus
Highlands of Costa Rica and Panama   5 in.

ROSE-BREASTED CHAT ♂
Granatellus pelzelni
Venezuela to Bolivia   5½ in.

HOODED WARBLER ♂
Wilsonia citrina
Eastern United States   5½ in.

PROTHONOTARY ♂
WARBLER
Protonotaria citrea
Eastern United States   5½ in.

Warbler. Further study of these hybrids is needed, but apparently they are fertile and their genetics follow Mendelian lines. More rarely intergeneric hybrids are reported, a recent one being Sutton's Warbler, thought to be a cross between the Parula and Yellow-throated warblers.

With a few exceptions, such as the 7½-inch Yellow-breasted Chat, the largest member of the family, which is strong-voiced and an excellent mimic, the warblers are not outstanding singers. Their voices are weak, high, and insect-like, often with hissing, buzzing, or lisping qualities. Yet the warblers are persistent singers in spring, and each species has a distinctive song of its own. The expert tells warblers apart by their songs as readily as by their appearance, but the notes of some species are so similar that it takes a sharp ear to differentiate between them. Among the more distinctive and easily recognized are the ringing "teacher, teacher, teacher" of the Ovenbird, the thin "witchitee-witchitee-witchitee-widgit" of the Yellow-throat, and the lisping "zee-zee-zee-zee-zee-zewo" of the Redstart.

Though many species of warblers throng together during migration, each species shows decided habitat preferences in summer, less so in winter. The well-named Pine Warbler is always associated with pines during the breeding season, and almost invariably nests in a clump of pine needles, seldom in other evergreens. The Blackpoll Warbler nests only in spruce and larch. The Chestnut-sided Warbler is fond of second-growth deciduous woodlands, and has increased markedly in the Appalachian region, where deserted farms are reverting to hardwood forest.

The wide-ranging Myrtle Warbler, with its bright-yellow rump patch, shows less partiality, but usually nests in conifer forests. It migrates and winters in more open country, and is common in the coastal belt of myrtle, whose waxy berries are its winter mainstay—bayberry in the north, wax myrtle farther south. The Magnolia Warbler is another inhabitant of northern spruce, hemlock, and balsam forests at nesting time. Its discoverer, the pioneering Alexander Wilson, collected the type specimen in a magnolia tree in Mississippi and gave it its inappropriate name.

A number of other warblers were given most unfitting names by their describers, who often christened them for the place where they discovered the bird in transit, far from its customary haunts. The Connecticut, Kentucky, Cape

May, Tennessee, and Nashville warblers are victims of such misnaming. The Prairie Warbler inhabits scrublands and seldom visits open prairies. The Palm Warbler breeds across palmless southern Canada and winters from Florida southward, not in palms, but in open fields and scrublands. Efforts to change these and other ill-fitting common names always meet stern resistance.

One of the rarest warblers and most restricted in its breeding range is Kirtland's Warbler, which nests only in a portion of the Michigan jackpine country less than 80 miles in diameter and migrates to the Bahama Islands. A careful census made in 1951 showed the total Kirtland's Warbler population to be less than a thousand individuals, and the species seems to be barely holding its own. A major limiting factor is parasitism by the Brown-headed Cowbird (p. 267). All wood warblers are among the cowbirds' most favored victims, but more than half the breeding Kirtland's Warblers rear young cowbirds instead of their own offspring.

Most temperate zone warblers build an open cup nest in the branches of shrubs or trees at moderate heights. Some treetop species, the Blackburnian, Cerulean, and Pine warblers for instance, may build 50 or more feet up, but most nest less than 10 feet above the ground, and some species nest on the ground. One northern ground-nesting species, the Ovenbird, is so called because of its oven-shaped domed nest with a side entrance. Among the very few cavity nesters in the family is the Prothonotary Warbler, one of our brightest golden-yellow birds. An inhabitant of the swamp lands of the southern states, the Prothonotary nests in holes in rotten stubs, sometimes in old woodpecker holes or bird boxes. The Catholic Louisiana Creoles christened it the Prothonotary in honor of the papal secretary, who traditionally wears a brilliant orange-yellow robe.

The breeding behavior of wood warblers follows fairly standard patterns. Nest building is almost entirely by the female, with occasional help from the male in a few species. Warbler eggs are generally white, lightly speckled with

BLACK-THROATED ♂
BLUE WARBLER
Dendroica caerulescens
Eastern North America 5 in.

PAINTED REDSTART
Setophaga picta
Arizona to Nicaragua 5 in.

brown, often in a ring around the larger end. The northern migratory species lay 4 to 5 eggs and are usually single-brooded. Incubation is always by the female alone, and sometimes, though not regularly, the male feeds her on the nest. Incubation takes 11 to 14 days, and the nestling period another 8 to 14 days.

Warblers migrate at night and frequently come to grief during their long journeys, usually from adverse weather conditions that catch the flocks in transit. Though the migrants take off under clear skies with favorable winds, they have no weather service to warn them of what lies ahead. Occasionally hurricanes carry them far off course and drop them exhausted into the sea. More often the migrants encounter weather fronts of low-lying clouds that force them close to the ground where they collide in the dark with TV towers, buildings, bridges, and other tall obstructions.

Bright lights attract and confuse night migrants forced below their normal flight altitude. Lighthouses on well-traveled flight paths have long been known to lure migrants to their death on foggy nights. The powerful searchlights used at airports to measure the height of cloud ceilings constitute a new and most destructive hazard. On drizzly nights swarms of migrating warblers, vireos, tanagers, and other species fly into the intense vertical beam. Unable to escape from the beam, they mill around within it in a cloud, crash into one another, and flutter helplessly to the ground in a rain of dying birds.

As yet we have no accurate measure of the mortality imposed by hazards of migration. At times this must be tremendous, and of serious import to species survival. Truckloads of tiny dead birds have been shoveled away under a ceilometer beam after a disastrous night. Countless thousands of additional migrants must perish during storms and other perils of nature. One such debacle during a mass flight could easily wipe out Kirtland's Warbler.

The Parulinae are well represented in tropical Central and South America south as far as Argentina, and in the West Indies, where they are more plentiful in the wooded high-

MAGNOLIA WARBLER ♂
Dendroica magnolia
Canada   5 in.

BANANAQUIT
Coereba flaveola
West Indies; Mexico to Argentina   4½ in.

lands than in wet lowlands. The two commonest tropical genera are *Myioborus* with some 8 species, and *Basileuterus* with about 22. While some of these are fairly brightly colored, most tend to be dull browns and yellows. The sexes are alike, and they show no marked seasonal plumage change as do the migratory species. Many build domed nests on or near the ground. Though the males do not incubate, they take an active part in nest building and other breeding chores. These sedentary species are not subject to the hazards of migration, and their reproductive rate is both lower and slower than in the northern breeders. The usual clutch is 2 to 3 eggs, incubation lasts 13 to 16 days, and the rearing period takes 12 to 14 days.

Another tropical group is the Coerebinae, which live mostly in lowland forests, and whose tongues are cleft and fringed for nectar feeding. Typical is the widespread Bananaquit, found from the Bahamas, throughout the West Indies (it is strangely absent from Cuba), and from southeastern Mexico southward to Paraguay and Argentina. These bright little birds are resident throughout their wide range and are often quite abundant. Local populations vary considerably in color, and some 35 subspecies are now recognized.

Except that they feed extensively on nectar by piercing the base of large flowers with their pointed curved bills, Bananaquits act much like warblers. They flit actively through the foliage in search of food, singly or in pairs, never in flocks. They also consume insects in quantity. Despite their name they are not overly fond of bananas, though they eat some other fruits such as sapodillas. Their voices are thin and warblerlike.

Bananaquits lay 2 to 6 eggs in a bulky domed nest with a side entrance near the bottom, usually in a thicket and fairly near the ground. While only the female incubates, the male is most active at nest building. He not only builds most of the nest, which the female lines and finishes for the eggs, but often builds a series of roosting nests nearby in which he spends the night.

ICTERIDS

PASSERIFORMES   ICTERIDAE

The 94 species of icterids include such common and familiar North American birds as blackbirds, grackles, orioles, meadowlarks, cowbirds, and the Bobolink. Less familiar tropical forms are the troupials, oropendolas, and caciques (ka-seeks'). None of these distinctive groups is truly representative of the entire family, and the names oriole, blackbird, and grackle are confused with Old World species. The term troupials has been used as a family name (this South American oriole was the first to be described), but has never become popular. Ornithologists always refer to these birds as the icterids, and that term is now widely used among amateurs as a convenient label for this all-American family. "Icter" being Latin for yellow, the name best fits the bright-yellow or orange orioles, but yellows occur throughout the family.

The icterids are small- to (typically) medium-sized birds, 6 to 21 inches in length. An integral part of the complex of New World nine-primaried oscines, they are so closely allied to the tanagers and to the cardinal finches that it is difficult to demark all three groups. The icterids lack obvious rictal bristles; most have rounded tails. Their wings are long and pointed, their legs and feet strong, their bills hard, conical and pointed. In the orioles and grackles the bill is moderately slender and down-curved. The oropendolas and caciques have heavier bills topped by a prominent swelling. Meadowlarks' bills are straight and sharp, as are most blackbirds'; those of the cowbirds and the Bobolink are short and finchlike.

The family ranges over all the Western Hemisphere except the extreme north, but is chiefly tropical. Most of its temperate zone members are migratory. Northernmost of the family is the Rusty Blackbird, which nests across the continent from the tree line to the northern United States, often in hemlock and larch swamps, and winters south to the Gulf Coast. The southernmost icterids are the red-breasted, or military, blackbirds of Patagonia. One of these inhabits the Falkland Islands, and another population thrives on Easter Island, where it was introduced.

Icterids have adapted themselves to almost all upland habitats. Most are arboreal, and various species can be found in almost every type of forest, from the Hudsonian conifers to tropical jungle. The meadowlarks and the Bobolink prefer open fields and prairies. The wide-ranging Red-winged Blackbirds and their close relatives, the Yellow-headed and Yellow-shouldered blackbirds, are essentially marsh dwellers. Scott's Oriole is at home in western semideserts among the agaves and yuccas.

Icterid food preferences are just as varied. All of them eat insects, and most eat seeds and grains. The tropical orioles and oropendolas are fruit eaters, as are the caciques, which also eat nectar. The grackles are practically omnivorous. Inveterate nest robbers, they also like small reptiles and amphibians, and some have learned to catch small fish.

Icterids that feed on the ground walk about vigorously and seldom hop. All are strong fliers. Their voices are usually loud, somewhat harsh, and vary from guttural burblings to clear, flutey whistles. Song is highly developed in the orioles. Most of the family are gregarious, many species highly so. The migrant temperate zone species travel and winter in flocks and sometimes roost in tremendous swarms. The oropendolas, caciques, and many blackbirds and grackles are colonial in their nesting.

The family exhibits great divergence in breeding habits, but the nesting duties fall largely on the female, entirely so in many groups. As often happens in markedly dichromatic groups where the males take little part in nesting, many species are promiscuous or polygamous. One group, the cowbirds, has developed brood parasitism to a high degree. Most icterids build conventional open cup nests, either in trees, on the ground, or in marsh vegetation, but the long, hanging nests of the orioles and their immediate kin are marvels of avian architecture. Icterid eggs are usually white, sometimes

**1 CHESTNUT-HEADED ♂
(WAGLER'S) OROPENDOLA**
Zarhynchus wagleri
Mexico to Ecuador   14 in.

2 GREEN OROPENDOLA ♂
Psarocolius viridis
The Guianas to
Ecuador and Peru   17 in.

3 MONTEZUMA OROPENDOLA ♂
Gymnostinops montezuma
Mexico to Panama   19 in.

4 TROUPIAL ♂
Icterus icterus
Colombia and Venezuela   9½ in.

5 SPOT-BREASTED ORIOLE ♂
Icterus pectoralis
Mexico to Costa Rica   8½ in.

tinted blue, green, or buff, and typically marked with heavy, irregular black scrawls. In the tropical species the normal clutch is 2 eggs; the temperate forms lay 3 to 7.

Gaudiest of the icterids, as well as among the best singers and nest architects, are the orioles. Some 30 species are grouped in the nominate genus *Icterus,* most of them tropical. The several that come north to nest in spring bring splashes of tropical splendor to the temperate woodlands, and the males' songs are rich, varied, and full-throated. In the tropical orioles the females are often as brightly colored as the males. The temperate zone females lack the males' gay hues. After breeding the males shed their finery and assume a similar drab dress before migrating.

The male Baltimore Oriole arrives in the eastern woodlands of the United States in spring, flaunting the strong orange and black of Maryland's founding family, the Calverts. His mate is quietly dressed in variable yellowish olives and browns. The Baltimore Oriole is replaced in the west by the similar, but specifically distinct, Bullock's Oriole. Where the two species overlap in Oklahoma and Nebraska they frequently hybridize. A less showy northern nester is the smaller Orchard Oriole, clad in quieter orange-brown and black. A fine singer in spring, the Orchard Oriole is one of our most useful insectivores.

The pair bond is strong in these orioles, but the males take little part in nesting. They spend their time chasing insects and singing while their mates weave the intricate cradles every farm boy knows, and lay and incubate the 4 to 6 eggs. The nest of the Baltimore Oriole is a neat gray bag of fibers about 6 inches deep with a constricted top; it is usually hung from the outer branches of a tall shade tree.

Among the world's best nest builders are the orioles' larger tropical relatives, the oropendolas and caciques. They weave marvelous long sleeves of grasses with the entrance at the top, the nest proper resting in a pouch at the bottom 3 to 6 feet below. They usually nest in colonies, which are fascinating and noisy bazaars. A colony of Montezuma's Oropendolas above my camp in British Honduras was never still. Throughout the day the birds kept up a continual bubbling chatter, the main theme of which sounded like "bottle-o-glooo."

For their colony these birds pick a tall isolated tree in a clearing or one towering above the surrounding jungle. Under a canopy of the tree's spreading top the female oropendolas weave from a dozen to a hundred long, swaying stockings that can be seen for miles around. The females outnumber the polygynous males, which sit around the top of the tree and act as guardians and watchmen, for they are faithful to the colony if not to a particular mate.

Polygyny occurs in most icterids that nest colonially and in some that do not. It varies in degree between populations of the same species, depending on the sex ratio. In Brewer's Blackbird of western North America the males are polygynous when outnumbered by the females, but not when the sexes are evenly balanced. The same is true of the Boat-tailed Grackles, and of the familiar Red-winged Blackbird.

The Redwing, with its prominent scarlet epaulets, breeds throughout southern Canada and the United States and southward through the West Indies and Central America. It is replaced in South America by the Yellow-shouldered Blackbird. In the sloughs of the prairie states nests the equally unmistakable Yellow-headed Blackbird. All these birds are highly gregarious; they migrate and winter in flocks, and usually nest colonially, in fresh-water marshes.

In temperate North America the male Redwings are one of the first migrants to arrive in spring, several weeks in advance of their mates. They have usually established their individual territories by the time the smaller and less conspicuous females appear. The last to arrive are the young of the previous year. It is not as yet certain to what extent Redwings breed in their first spring, if at all.

Usually the sexes are evenly balanced and monogamy is the rule, but it is not unusual to find two or more females nesting within the territory of a single male. Nest building and incubation are by the female alone, though the male is attentive throughout the process, and helps feed the young.

The nest is an open cup, woven of coarse grasses in the marsh vegetation, usually only a few feet above the water or ground. Incubation and fledging each take about 12 days.

The young birds in their first juvenile plumage resemble the female, but the sexes are distinguishable by both size and color. In the annual postnuptial molt an adult male's distinctive black garb is hidden by brown tips to the feathers. These gradually wear off during the winter to reveal his nuptial dress beneath; there is no second molt in spring.

As the nesting season ends, first the young birds and later the adult Redwings flock to the uplands to feed in open fields, returning to the shelter of the marsh at night. In migration, flocks coalesce and increase in size. On the wintering grounds in the southern states they join with other flocking blackbirds. Five or six species often roost together in tremendous aggregations of millions of birds.

The birds leave the roosts at dawn and travel as much as 30 to 50 miles in search of good foraging. By mid-afternoon they start heading toward the roost, and converge on it from all directions. The vanguard arrives several hours before dark, and from then on flock after flock pour in until darkness. Roosts of several hundred thousand birds are common, and some of the larger roosts in Alabama and Arkansas have been estimated to contain 5 million birds. Flocks of this size can and do inflict serious damages to grain crops, and this is only partly compensated for by the large numbers of insects the birds also consume. Wholesale killing is sometimes used as a control measure.

Most notorious of the crop damagers used to be the Bobolink, the champion icterid migrant. Bobolinks breed across southern Canada and the northern United States and winter in Argentina, migrating both north and south across the Gulf of Mexico and the Caribbean. In the days of horses, when hay was a standard crop, Bobolinks were common summer residents in New England farmlands. Now that hayfields are few, the species has almost disappeared from the Northeast, but has expanded its range westward. The western Bobolinks retrace their steps eastward in migration before heading southward across the Gulf.

The Bobolinks' breeding pattern is similar to the Redwings'. Males arrive on the breeding grounds before the females and establish territories. Females build cup nests well concealed on the ground in upland grassy fields. The species is occasionally polygynous, and rears but a single brood of 5 to 7 young.

When rice was a major commercial crop in the Carolinas in the 19th and early 20th centuries, migrating Bobolinks were a serious pest to the sprouting seeds in spring and to the maturing grain in fall. They were killed by the thousands to protect the crops, and marketed as "reed birds" or "rice birds." The fall migrants are very fat, and they were brought to market skewered a dozen to a stick. In Jamaica, where they stop on their cross-water flight, they are still called "butter birds." Now the Bobolink is protected as a song bird, and "rice birds" are no longer available for the gourmet. Rice growing has shifted to Louisiana and Texas, where other flocking icterids, notably the Redwing, are occasionally equally harmful to the crops.

Among the North American icterids perhaps the most highly regarded as insect destroyers and as sweet singers are the meadowlarks. They pipe their clear whistles all year, though most ardently at breeding time, and have none of the annoying habits of their more gregarious relatives. They never gather in such large flocks, and they do not attack standing grain. Their vegetable food in fall and winter is confined to weed seeds and waste grain left in the fields after harvesting. They are not strongly migratory, and will winter as far north as they can find snow-free fields.

The two species, the Eastern and Western meadowlarks, are so similar in appearance they are almost impossible to tell apart by size and color alone. The Western Meadowlark is only slightly smaller than the Eastern, its yellow breast is slightly paler, and the yellow of its throat extends slightly farther into the cheek. These differences are almost useless

1 BOBOLINK ♂
Dolichonyx oryzivorus
Eastern North America 8 in.

2 RED-BREASTED BLACKBIRD ♂
Leistes militaris
Panama to Argentina 7½ in.

3 YELLOW-HEADED BLACKBIRD ♂
Xanthocephalus xanthocephalus
Western North America 11 in.

4 SHINY COWBIRD ♂
Molothrus bonariensis
Colombia and Venezuela to Argentina 7–8 in.

6 BOAT-TAILED GRACKLE ♂
Cassidix mexicanus
Southern U.S. to Venezuela and Peru 17 in.

5 WESTERN MEADOWLARK
Sturnella neglecta
Western North America 9 in.

as field marks, and where both species occur observers depend on their voices to tell one from the other. The Western Meadowlarks' call note is of a different timbre and a full kilocycle lower than the Eastern's, and differences in phrasing and syllabification in the two species' clear, plaintive songs are easily recognized.

Recent studies in Wisconsin, where both Meadowlark species often nest at the same time in the same field, show they apparently do not hybridize in the wild. Their breeding habits are identical and resemble those of the Bobolink. They differ almost imperceptibly in their choice of nesting sites, the Eastern Meadowlark choosing moister spots in the meadows; the Western drier ones. The females have the major role in selecting their mates, and invariably choose males of their own species. They apparently base their unerring choice on differences in voice rather than of appearance or behavior.

Breeding aberrations among the icterids are most pronounced in the cowbirds, which have brought brood parasitism to the same perfection in the New World as the cuckoos, honeyguides, and a few weaverfinches have in the Old. Cowbirds are well named, for they habitually hang around cattle. Before livestock were brought to this country, the cowbirds followed the herds of buffaloes. Except for the Giant Cowbird of Central and South America, which hunts hides for ticks just as do the oxpeckers of Africa, cowbirds seldom alight on cattle, but flock around to feed on the insects disturbed by their feet.

The degrees of parasitism exhibited by different cowbird species are of particular interest because they suggest how the habit probably developed. The first step apparently was the loss of the inclination, and then of the ability, to build a nest. The nonparasitic Baywinged Cowbird of Brazil and Argentina is at present in this stage. While some individuals can and do occasionally build nests of their own, they are reluctant to do so and prefer to use the abandoned nests of other species.

The next stage, that of dispossessing the owner from a freshly built nest, is evidently quite transitory, and no species shows it today. At this point the birds must learn quickly to leave their eggs for the rightful owner to hatch and rear, but they do not immediately lose all the ingrained habits of nesting behavior. The widespread Shiny Cowbird of South America, which is parasitic on many small birds, occasionally shows nesting instincts during courtship. Birds pick up nesting material, and sometimes start to build a nest, but they never finish one. Nor has the Shiny Cowbird yet learned to put its eggs out efficiently for adoption. Females waste many eggs by laying them on the ground when they are unable to find a nest, and often put more eggs in a single nest than the foster parent can care for. As many as 37 Shiny Cowbird eggs have been found in one ovenbird's nest.

Some cowbirds have developed host-specificity. The Screaming Cowbird of Brazil and Argentina relies entirely on the nonparasitic Baywinged Cowbird to rear its young for it. The Giant Cowbird chooses oropendolas and caciques for its dupes. The Redeyed, or Bronze, Cowbird of the southwestern United States and Mexico is not so particular. While it specializes in victimizing various orioles, its eggs have been found in the nests of a number of non-icterids. Least selective in its choices and most successful as a brood parasite is the Brown-headed Cowbird of temperate North America. Its eggs have been found in nests of more than 200 other species, mostly smaller birds such as vireos, warblers, and various seedeaters.

Though they shirk the nesting chores, like most other icterids Brown-headed Cowbirds establish breeding territories. They are usually monogamous, though polygyny is thought to occur when there is an excess of females. The female cowbird watches prospective hosts building their nests within her territory, and seems to know in advance where she is going to lay. She usually lays 4 to 5 eggs, each on successive mornings, and each in a different nest unless hosts are scarce. Also she lays as the hosts are still laying and before incubation has started. Unlike the cuckoo, she does not remove an egg when depositing her own, but occasionally returns and removes some, though never all, of the host's eggs.

The Brown-headed Cowbird egg hatches in 11 to 12 days, which is seldom longer than the time it takes the eggs of its hosts to hatch. Nor does the young cowbird push other eggs or nestlings out of the nest, as do nestling cuckoos. Being larger than the young of most of its small hosts, it does manage to get most of the food and fledges more rapidly, usually in 9 to 10 days. Thus while cowbird parasitism greatly reduces the reproductive efficiency of its victims, it does not negate it entirely. There are many records of 2 or 3 other young birds reared successfully in the nest with the cowbird, and this seems to be the general pattern. But reducing the annual production of young by 60 percent, as cowbird parasitism does to Kirtland's Warbler, can be serious in a species of such low numbers and limited distribution.

TANAGERS

PASSERIFORMES   THRAUPIDAE

"Tanager" is another of the distinctive New World bird names, such as jaçana, jacamar, jabiru, anhinga, ani, araçari, toucan, tinamou, hoatzin, macaw, seriema, and cotinga, that have come into our language from that of the Tupi Indians of the Amazon region. The Tupis, who have always been pretty good bird watchers, call these gaudy arboreal birds tangaras, which 18th century European systematists Latinized as tanagra. "Tanager," the English version, has been in common use since early in the 19th century.

The tanager family is a large one of some 223 species confined almost entirely to the tropical and subtropical portions of the Americas. All but the four species that have pushed

FLAME-FACED TANAGER
Tangara parzudakii
Colombia to Peru   6 in.

SCARLET-RUMPED TANAGER ♂
Ramphocelus passerinii
Mexico to Panama   7 in.

BLUE-GRAY TANAGER
Thraupis virens
Mexico to Brazil

SCARLET TANAGER ♂
Piranga olivacea
Eastern North America   7 in.

TANAGERS   269

into temperate North America to breed are nonmigratory, though some of the Central and South American highland tanagers wander altitudinally with the seasons. Gay colors the year round are a hallmark of the family, and female tanagers are usually as brightly colored as the males. Strong sex differences occur in the four migrant species and in the few tropical forms that flock together when not nesting, such as the velvet tanagers and the euphonias. The northern tanagers are among the few that show any seasonal plumage change. In a few genera both sexes are dull, soft browns or brownish reds and greens, but most are as colorful as tropical birds are supposed to be.

The tanagers are small- to medium-sized birds, most of them less than 8 inches in length, and compactly built. Their wings, with nine primaries, vary in length and shape, but are usually short and rounded. The presence of obvious rictal bristles separates the tanagers from the icterids, but not from the cardinal finches, to which they seem more closely allied. Tanagers differ from sparrows (fringillids) mainly in their adaptations to a fruit or nectar diet.

The 191 "typical" tanagers of the subfamily Thraupinae have a simple tongue and a fairly distinctive bill. It is short to medium in length, somewhat conical, curved downward along the top ridge, and has a small notch or tooth in the cutting edge near the slightly hooked tip. Best known are the four North American species of the genus *Piranga* that winter southward to their ancestral home in the tropics. These are the Scarlet Tanager of the East and Midwest, the Western Tanager of the western states, and the Summer and Hepatic tanagers of the southern United States and northern Mexico.

Despite the males' showy colors these tanagers are not conspicuous. They live quietly at moderate heights in the leafy shadows and do not call attention to themselves by action or voice. In the north their food is principally leaf-eating insects with smaller amounts of fruit and berries. They catch flying insects on the wing and forage efficiently, but without dash or hurry. Their songs are pleasant and musical but not distinctive. The northern tanagers build loose cup-shaped nests well concealed on a horizontal branch. They lay 3 to 5 greenish-blue eggs blotched and spotted with brown. Incubation, which is by the female alone, takes 13 to 15 days. The male helps feed the young, which require another 2 weeks to fledge.

The eight species of velvet tanagers of the genus *Ramphocelus,* found from Mexico to Argentina, are a tropical group in which the sexes differ. The males of this genus (the Scarlet-rumped Tanager is an example) are glossy, velvety black, variously marked with reds or yellows, and have bright silvery-blue bills. The females are nondescript brownish birds.

The Scarlet-rumped Tanager is one of the better singers in this family. Its songs are notable for length and persistence rather than for musical quality. The females do not sing, but start to build their open cup nests soon after the males come into voice at the start of the rainy season. The species shows little territorial sense, and pairs often nest in groups fairly close together in the lower branches of the forest edges. The female builds the nest, though the male occasionally accompanies her on her trips for material, which she often steals from the nests of other birds. The female incubates unassisted, though her mate usually helps rear the young.

The nominate genus *Thraupis* contains eight fairly large and common tanagers, 7 to 8 inches long, known as "blue tanagers." The sexes are alike, and predominantly blue in color, as in the Blue-gray Tanager. Though they live in the treetops, these active tanagers are easily observed in partly cleared and cultivated areas. They eat fruit and berries, and are adept insect catchers.

When not nesting the blue tanagers sometimes gather in small flocks, but they remain mated throughout the year and usually go about in pairs. Their breeding habits are similar to those of the northern migratory tanagers, but they lay a smaller clutch of 2 to 3 eggs and rear at least two broods annually. The incubation period is from 12 to 14 days, but the young take longer to fledge—up to 20 days.

The 48 species assigned to the genus *Tangara,* which have spread throughout Central and South America, are the epitome of typical tropical tanagers. The sexes are alike in these fruit and insect eaters. Their beauty is feather deep, for they have little or no song.

Best studied and one of the commonest of the *Tangaras* is the Golden-masked Tanager, found from southern Mexico southward through the Amazon basin. It lives in the wet rainforests and in open fields from sea level up to 5,000 feet. It is usually encountered in pairs, for the species stays mated the year round. The Golden-masked Tanager builds an open cup nest well hidden in the foliage anywhere from 5 to 50 feet up. Both sexes work on the nest, but only the female incubates the 2-egg clutch. Incubation takes 13 to 15 days, and the male feeds her on the nest. He also helps feed the young and is very active about it. After a fledging period of about 14 to 16 days, the young leave the nest in a plumage similar to but duller than their parents'. This they soon replace in a postjuvenile molt by the regular adult dress. These little birds rear 2 or 3 broods each nesting season, which extends in Central America from February to September.

The genus *Tangara* contains several rare species known by only one or two specimens and never seen in life by an ornithologist. Their skins were found in shipments of bright-colored birds sent to the European markets during the feather-trade days of the 1880's. Gould's Tanager, a distinctive green, blue, yellow, and black bird, known by a single specimen in the British Museum, is thought to have come from southeastern Brazil. Arnault's Tanager is a unique buff, green, blue, and black. The only known specimen, which is in a Paris museum, reached Europe alive as a cage bird. Just where in South America it came from is unknown. Ornithologists have long searched in vain for these and other little-known birds which may still exist as small isolated populations in the vast forests of the American tropics.

A third rarity, the Azure-rumped, or Cabanis's, Tanager, was described in 1866 from a single trade skin that came from western Guatemala and is now in the Berlin Museum. It is a 6-inch bird with back and rump azure green, crown and neck grayish blue, and wings and tail black, edged with blue. Dr. Pierce Brodkorb of the University of Florida had

**BLUE-CROWNED ♂
CHLOROPHONIA**
Chlorophonia occipitalis
Mexico to Panama   5½ in.

MASKED TANAGER
Tangara nigro-cincta
Mexico to Bolivia   5¼ in.

PARADISE TANAGER
Tangara chilensis
Colombia to Brazil and Bolivia   5¾ in.

the once-in-a-lifetime thrill of rediscovering Cabanis's long-lost tanager in Chiapas, southern Mexico, in 1937.

Another large complex of tanagers found from Mexico southward are the 24 small euphonias, whose generic name *Tanagra* is confused with *Tangara* by proofreaders—and others. The euphonias are dumpy little birds, most under 5 inches, with short tails and stubby bills. Unlike most tropical tanagers, the males are prettily patterned in shining dark blues and yellows but the females are dull olive-greens. The Yellow-winged Euphonia is an example.

Euphonias roam along the forest edges in pairs or small bands searching for berries and small fruits. A favorite food is mistletoe berries. They differ from the larger tanagers in building domed nests, which are chiefly the work of the female, though the male sometimes lends a hand. In true tanager fashion the female does all the incubating (13 to 14 days), and the male helps feed the young. The members of this group feed their young by regurgitation. The parents stand at the nest's entrance and pop berry after berry into the mouths of the nestlings. As in all tanagers the inside of the

YELLOW-CROWNED ♂
EUPHONIA
Tanagra luteicapilla
Nicaragua to Panama   4 in.

RED-CROWNED ♂
ANT TANGER
Habia rubica
Mexico to Argentina   7 in.

nestlings' mouths is bright red, and this is believed to stimulate the parents' feeding reaction. The fledging period in the tanagers that build covered nests is considerably longer than in the open nesters, and lasts up to 23 or 24 days.

Closely related to the euphonias are the four slightly larger chlorophonias, 5½ to 6 inches long. The males of these stub-billed tanagers are beautifully tinted in greens, blues, and yellows, the females similar but paler and duller. Chlorophonias (their generic name) are highland dwellers, found for the most part in cloud forests above 4,000 feet. Their habits are essentially those of the euphonias. Their clutch is usually three eggs, and they are double-brooded.

A second branch of the tanager family is the 28 honey-creepers and flower-piercers of the subfamily Dacninae. These birds have longer, more slender bills than the typical tanagers, and brush-tipped tongues. They are still classified by some workers, together with the bananaquit, in a separate family, but their palate structure and musculature show them to be tanagers modified for nectar feeding.

The Blue, or Red-legged, Honeycreeper ranges widely from Cuba and southern Mexico to Ecuador and southern Brazil, and is often encountered in small flocks. A bird of the treetops and forest edges, it is commonest in the humid lowlands. The female is a dull olive-green above and yellowish below. In a postnuptial molt the male takes on a similar dull green dress, which is gradually replaced with bright blue and yellow before the next breeding season.

Honeycreepers use their long, thin pointed bills to gather flower nectar, always while perched, never while hovering. They also eat some fruit and small insects. Their breeding patterns resemble those of the true tanagers. Nest building and incubation (12 to 13 days) are by the female, and the male usually follows her about as she works, but is not attentive to her during incubation. He does help bring fruit and insects to the young, which take 2 weeks to fledge. Food is brought in the bill and is not regurgitated. In Central America the Blue Honeycreeper builds an open cup nest of fine fibers tied together with spider webs, and lays two spotted white eggs.

Most specialized of the nectar-eating tanagers are the dull-brownish diglossas, or flower-piercers, whose bills are peculiarly and uniquely adapted for their particular method of feeding. The upper mandible is bent upward and strongly hooked at the tip. With this the bird holds the tubular corolla firm while it pierces it with the needle-like lower mandible, and then inserts its tongue for the nectar. The operation takes only a moment, and the birds can sip from a number of blossoms in a short time. Aided by their strong rictal bristles, diglossas also catch small insects on the wing.

The 10 species of flower-piercers are highland dwellers found from southern Mexico to Peru and Bolivia and eastward to Venezuela and the Guianas. They forage alone or in pairs, and both sexes sing a thin, weak, trilling song. The female builds a thick-walled cup nest of mosses in low bushes for her two bright-blue eggs, spotted with brown, which she incubates alone.

Three other aberrant species I have placed with the tanagers as a matter of convenience may each warrant family rank. These are the Swallow Tanager (*Tersina*), the Thrush Tanager (*Rhodinocichla*), and the Plush-capped Tanager (*Catamblyrhynchus*). All three are in need of further study.

The Swallow Tanager has been studied more than the other two species. Tanager-like in appearance, the male is a lovely, soft greenish-blue, the female a plainer green. Found from Panama southward through Amazonia, it seems to be partly migratory. Small flocks wander through the lowland treetops, and move to higher country to breed. The species' chief peculiarities are its wide, flat bill, sharp-edged and strongly hooked at the tip, and its distendable throat pouch. This bulges out in weird shapes when the bird stuffs it with fruit. Swallow Tanagers have prodigious appetites, and captive birds will eat two-thirds of their weight in fruit daily. They also catch insects on the wing. Their voices are monotonous, unmusical chirps, and they have no song.

RED-LEGGED HONEYCREEPER ♂
Cyanerpes cyaneus
Cuba; Mexico to Ecuador and Brazil 4½ in.

The Swallow Tanager differs from most other tanagers in being a cavity nester. Its nest is in a natural hole in a tree. In some parts of their range the birds dig tunnels into earthen banks, or use cavities in houses or stone walls. Nest building and incubation of the 3 glossy white eggs are by the female alone. Incubation varies from 13 to 17 days, and starts with the laying of the first egg, so the chicks hatch on successive days. The male helps feed the young, which take up to 24 days to fledge.

The Thrush Tanager is a skulking bird of the forest floor found from Mexico to Colombia and Venezuela. It is difficult to see despite its bright, soft red colors because it stays in the shadowy underbrush. Anatomically it seems closest to the tanagers, but in behavior it shows strong similarities to the thrashers and the cardinal finches. Thrush Tanagers feed on the ground, flicking away among the leaves like thrashers.

CINNAMON-BELLIED ♂
FLOWER-PIERCER
Diglossa baritula
Mexico to Honduras   4½ in.

SWALLOW TANAGER ♂
Tersina viridis
Panama to Argentina   6¼ in.

PLUSH-CAPPED TANAGER
Catamblyrhynchus diadema
Colombia and Venezuela
to Peru and Bolivia   5 in.

ROSE-BREASTED ♂
THRUSH TANAGER
Rhodinocichla rosea
Mexico to Venezuela   8 in.

They have a fine loud song which both sexes sing anti-phonally during courtship. Recent studies have shown that the male helps with the incubation as well as with other nesting duties.

Least known of the three is the peculiar Plush-capped Tanager, called the Plush-capped Finch by those who, with equally good justification, classify it with the cardinal finches. Found in high Andean forests, it is named for the unique patch of short, stiff, velvety, orange-yellow feathers on the forehead of both sexes, which are similar in color. The bill is short, stubby, and slightly hooked. Most of the specimens in museum collections are trade skins. Few ornithologists have ever encountered this bird in the field. It is usually seen alone or in pairs. Its feeding and nesting habits are unknown, and its anatomy has never been studied.

NEW WORLD SEEDEATERS

PASSERIFORMES   FRINGILLIDAE

At the top of the avian family tree is the tremendous galaxy of small- to medium-sized birds known collectively as sparrows or finches. The most recent estimate, which shows 690 species, may be in error by a score of species either way, depending on how a few poorly known forms are classified. The main characteristic of sparrows and finches is their short, conical, pointed bills, adapted principally for eating seeds.

From the evolutionary standpoint the seedeaters are a youthful as well as a dominant group. The seed-bearing plants that furnish their principal food came suddenly into prominence during the Miocene epoch, 25 or 30 million years ago. Other birds turned partially to this new type of food—larks among the passerines, and quail, pheasants, and pigeons among the nonpasserines. But none exploited seeds as food so intensively as did the ancestors of the sparrows. Seed-producing plants, principally grasses and sedges, spread rapidly after the Miocene. So did these small birds that relied on them for food. The presence of seeds allowed sparrows to populate almost all the land areas of the world. They are absent only from Antarctica, where no seed-bearing plants grow, and from a few oceanic islands the birds have been unable to reach.

The task of sorting the vast complex of seedeaters into natural groups that reflect their ancestry and relationships to one another has long plagued ornithologists. We are now certain that they arose from 2 or 3 parent stocks, perhaps more, simultaneously in different parts of the world. Complicating the problem has been the marked parallelism of anatomical development of the various groups. Another factor is the successful spread of these similar stocks between continents into each other's natal domains.

Seedeaters fall most logically and conveniently into two large families based on place of origin, the New World Fringillidae and the Old World Ploceidae. Sizable segments of each family occur today in both hemispheres, and some subfamilies in each family are often given full family rank.

The 315 or so seedeaters of New World origin are an integral part of the complex of Western Hemisphere oscines with nine primary feathers. Though the fringillids are the most youthful, widespread, and highly developed of this complex, many students consider them close to the ancestral stock from which they and the vireos, warblers, icterids, and tanagers have branched. New World sparrows are so close to the icterids and tanagers that some species are assigned to one family or another almost arbitrarily. The Dickcissel of our midwestern prairies, for instance, is generally regarded as a fringilline finch. It has also been placed, on good grounds, with the icterids and with the cardinal finches, which some anatomists now place with the tanagers. The lines of distinction, both anatomical and behavioral, between the three families are indeed fine. The fringillids' strong reliance on seeds as their main food (though there are exceptions) is a major one.

In addition to anatomical criteria involving the form and shape of the palate bones and the attachment and insertion of various head and limb muscles, fringillids show basic behavioral traits that unite them as a group and help to separate them from their Old World counterparts, the ploceids. Fringillids forage mostly on or near the ground. Most have a well-developed and pleasing song, which they usually give from a perch, rarely in flight. With few exceptions they are strong fliers, and most temperate zone species are migratory. Many are gregarious when not nesting. They migrate and winter in flocks.

None of the fringillids nests colonially, and their breeding habits are catholic, fairly uniform, and show few departures from the norm. Almost all build open cup nests, a very few high in trees, more in low bushes, in the grass, or on the ground. A few tropical species build covered nests, and members of one genus, the saffron finches, stuff them into cavities. All fringillids, so far as we know, are essentially monogamous, none is parasitic, and each pair establishes and defends a breeding territory of its own.

The family divides handily into three subfamilies—the cardinal finches (Richmondeninae), the small group of Galapagos, or Darwin's, finches (Geospizinae), and the nominate Fringillinae, which we usually call sparrows but the British call buntings. The collective names sparrow, finch, bunting, and grosbeak have been so widely and miscellaneously applied to various species of both fringillids and ploceids that they have no taxonomic significance.

The 35 species that constitute the cardinal finch subfamily have rather stocky bodies and stout, strong bills. Essentially arboreal woodland inhabitants, they show a number of other close similarities to tanagers. Though the females are sparrowy browns, the males of most species are brightly colored in reds or blues. They are not markedly

PYRRHULOXIA ♂
Pyrrhuloxia sinuata
Southwestern U.S., northern Mexico   8 in.

BLUE GROSBEAK ♂
Guiraca caerulea
Southern U.S.
to Costa Rica   6½ in.

CARDINAL ♂
Richmondena cardinalis
United States to southern Mexico   8 in.

PAINTED BUNTING ♂
Passerina ciris
Southern U.S. and
northern Mexico   5¼ in.

gregarious, and many species remain paired throughout the year. With few exceptions the female does all the incubating, though the male helps build the nest, often feeds the incubating female, and always helps rear the young. Most cardinal finches are better singers than tanagers, and they feed more on the ground. Their center of distribution is tropical America, and they range northward to southern Canada and southward to Argentina.

Most familiar of the northern members of the subfamily is the Cardinal, the well-loved "red bird" of our southern states. Found throughout the warm temperate parts of eastern North America and southward to Mexico and British

Honduras, the Cardinal's six geographical races tend to be resident, and the birds exhibit little seasonal movement. The Cardinal seems to be pushing its range slowly northward. It is now a fairly common resident in the New York area, where it was unknown when I did my youthful birding there not so long ago. Closely related to the Cardinal is the svelte Pyrrhuloxia found from Texas and southern Arizona southward through Mexico. It feeds more on the ground than does the Cardinal, and is seldom found far from cover.

Other members of this subfamily that have pushed northward from their tropical homes, such as the Rose-breasted and the Blue grosbeaks, are not so hardy, and retire southward to their ancestral tropics when winter comes. The Rose-breasted Grosbeak of deciduous woodlands in eastern North America and the Black-headed Grosbeak of western North America are exceptions to the usual breeding pattern of the group. The male does much of the incubating and often sings while doing so. The Black-headed Grosbeak is also known for its song flight during courtship, and is one of the few members of the entire family that sings on the wing.

The Blue-black Grosbeak is a dark-blue bird that ranges from Mexico to Bolivia. Both sexes sing to one another as they work at nest building. Incubation takes 13 to 14 days. The young are fed by both sexes and fledge in another 11 to 12 days. A South American representative is the Ultramarine Grosbeak, found from Venezuela down to temperate Argentina. Though the temperate zone grosbeaks all lay 4 eggs, the tropical species lay only 2 per clutch, but are multibrooded and may raise 3 broods each year.

Smallest and most colorful of the richmondenines are the six buntings of the genus *Passerina*. These range from the United States to Panama, and the three northern species, the Indigo, Lazuli, and Painted buntings, are migratory. The male Painted Bunting is one of the most startlingly bright birds in North America, and aptly justifies its commonly heard name of "nonpareil." The female is dull greenish above and yellowish below. In spite of its unequaled splashy colors,

BLACK-HEADED SALTATOR
Saltator atriceps
Mexico to Panama   10 in.

the nonpareil is not conspicuous, for it stays within the foliage of thickets. For a short time during the breeding season, the male sits out on an open perch and trills a musical little song to encourage his incubating mate and warn other nonpareils away from his breeding territory.

Most tanager-like of the cardinal finches in behavior are the 11 large, plain-colored sparrows known only by their generic name *Saltator*. The several species I have met in Central and South America are quiet, sedate, and unobtrusive. Largest of the genus is the Black-headed Saltator.

Better known is the slightly smaller 8-inch Buff-throated Saltator found from Mexico south to Paraguay.

Residents of the humid tropics, saltators live in open woodlands and at the edges of forest clearings. They are usually greenish brown above, lighter, sometimes streaked below, and have striking markings of white, yellow, or black about the head. The sexes are alike or closely similar. Their bills are large and finchlike, but not so stout and strong as those of cardinals and grosbeaks. While saltators eat some seeds, their diet is essentially berries and fruits, and many of them eat flowers. Another tanager characteristic is their voices, which are somewhat weak for such large, stout birds.

Saltators build a bulky open nest among the foliage fairly near the ground. Nest building and incubation are by the female, but the male stands by and attends her. Incubation of the 2-egg clutch takes 13 to 14 days. Both parents feed the

WOODPECKER FINCH ♂
Camarhynchus pallidus
Galapagos Isls. 5 in.

LARGE GROUND FINCH ♂
Geospiza magnirostris
Galapagos Isls. 5¾ in.

young, often for several weeks after they leave the nest following a 14-day fledging period. They are multibrooded.

The second subfamily, the Geospizinae, are most fittingly known as Darwin's finches, for Darwin discovered them when the *Beagle* visited the Galapagos Islands in 1835. His study of these birds, all similar enough to one another to show obvious relationship, yet each markedly different, was instrumental in convincing Darwin of the validity of the first great axiom in the formulation of his theory of evolution—that "species are not immutable."

Darwin's finches are a small, compact group of 14 species divided among 4 genera. They occur only on the Galapagos, the little group of islands on the equator 600 miles west of Ecuador, and on Cocos Island between the Galapagos and Panama. They are all believed to have descended from a single ancestor of early fringillid stock that managed to reach these islands from the American mainland, possibly in Pliocene time, say, 5 or 10 million years ago.

This little group of birds is one of the neatest, clearest, and most clear-cut examples of adaptive radiation—the process whereby the descendants of a single parent stock differentiate and radiate out to fill separate ecological niches close to one another. This process is seldom as apparent in the complex faunas of large land masses, where competition from unrelated forms is stiffer. Evolution works fastest in small isolated populations, away from competition. (Another example is the Hawaiian honeycreepers.)

Darwin's finches vary in size from 4 to 8 inches. In most species both sexes are colored alike in grayish browns; in some the males are black. They show their greatest divergences in their bills, which vary from stout and finchlike to long, thin, and warblerlike. Most of the stout-billed species live on seeds. The one with the smallest, thinnest bill lives on insects. One with a decurved bill and a split tongue probes the flowers of the prickly-pear cactus for nectar and eats its soft, pulpy fruit. One with a short, thick, slightly decurved bill lives on buds, leaves, and fruits. One with a stout, straight bill, the Woodpecker Finch, has developed one of the most amazing of all bird habits. Although it chisels into bark for insects, it lacks the woodpecker's long tongue to rake out the grups after it has opened their burrow. So it picks up a small sharp twig or a cactus thorn and probes with it into the burrow until the insect emerges. It then drops the thorn and grabs its meal. The only other known case of a bird using a tool is the bowerbirds' use of grass swabs for painting their bowers.

Despite the wide differences in their bills and feeding habits, studies of their internal anatomy have verified the close relationship of the Darwin's finches to each other. This is further indicated by their breeding habits, which are remarkably similar for a group with such diverse feeding habits. All establish nesting territories, which the males defend and advertise to the females with an unimpressive and not too musical song. All build covered nests, large for the size of the builder, usually out in the open near the end of a branch of a cactus or other growth, from 3 to 30 feet up. Though the eggs differ in size among the various species, all are white with pink spots, and the normal clutch is four eggs. Incubation takes 12 days by the female alone, and the young remain in the nest another 2 weeks. The male feeds the female on the nest and helps her feed the young.

The nominate Fringillinae, the third and last subfamily, is the largest and most widespread of all seedeater groups. It contains some 266 species of about 75 genera. They are most plentiful and best developed in the American tropics and subtropics, where the family is believed to have arisen. From this center the fringillines have dispersed to occupy all of the Americas south to Cape Horn and north to the frozen lands along the polar seas. Two genera, the longspurs (*Calcarius*) and the snow buntings (*Plectrophenax*), are completely circumpolar in the far north. Some 40 species of three strictly Old World genera have descended from an early invasion of the Eastern Hemisphere, perhaps in late Miocene or early Pliocene time. These are widespread over continental Eurasia, and a few have managed to push south-ward in Africa to the Cape of Good Hope. No fringillines have reached beyond the main Old World continents.

The fringilline finches are small birds from 4½ to 8 inches long. Most are clothed in inconspicuous browns, streaked or mottled with grays. Bright colors are rare. Their more striking patterns are formed by contrasting black and white, occasionally with spots of yellow. Usually the sexes are alike or closely similar. In a few the males are more gaily colored, such as the dichromatic black and white Lark Bunting of the North American prairie states with its drab brown mate, and the black, brown, and white Towhee, whose consort has a less conspicuous brown instead of black.

Most fringillines are birds of grasslands, scrublands, or open woodlands. Some inhabit forest undergrowth, but none

CHESTNUT-COLLARED
LONGSPUR ♂
Calcarius ornatus
Central North America 6½

WHITE-THROATED SPARROW
Zonotrichia albicollis
Northern North America 7 in.

LAPLAND LONGSPUR ♂
Calcarius lapponicus
Arctic tundra, circumpolar

is strictly arboreal. Though some nest in shrubs or low trees, most are ground nesters. All forage on or near the ground. Seeds of any and all sorts are their mainstay. To these they add small amounts of other vegetable matter—buds, foliage, or an occasional taste of fruit and berries in season—and varying quantities of insects to boost their protein intake. They feed their young almost exclusively on insects.

The 50-odd species that occur regularly in temperate North America include many familiar dooryard birds. The friendly Song and Chipping sparrows nest in shrubbery close to houses and sing cheerily in spring and summer. Relatives of the Song Sparrow are the Swamp and Lincoln's sparrows. Close congeners of the Chippy are the Field, Clay-colored, Brewer's, and Tree sparrows. Field inhabitants are the Lark Sparrow and the Vesper Sparrow (that sings by day as well as at

SNOW BUNTING ♂
Plectrophenax nivalis
Arctic tundra,
circumpolar

OREGON JUNCO
Junco oreganus
Western North America 6 in.

TREE SPARROW
Spizella arborea
Northern
North America 6½ in.

twilight), the widespread Savannah Sparrow, and the Grass-hopper Sparrow named for its insectlike buzzing trill.

A striking group is formed by the crowned *Zonotrichias*, the White-crowned, Golden-crowned, White-throated, and Harris sparrows, that breed in the northern woodlands. All are fine singers, and considered by many the prettiest of the sparrows. Less well known are the Seaside Sparrows of our eastern coastal marshes and the Sharp-tails that nest in fresh or brackish marshes. Then there are the Sage Sparrows of our western deserts, and the Black-chinned Sparrow of chaparral-covered hillsides, among many others.

Practically all these temperate zone breeders are migratory, most of them flocking in winter to the southern states and northern Central America. Many are hardy enough to withstand the northern winters. Such Canadian and Hudsonian zone breeders as the juncos, the Tree Sparrow, and the *Zonotrichias* winter commonly in fields and suburbs of the northern states, sometimes joined by the Snow Buntings and Lapland Longspurs that come down from the Arctic when the snows get deep.

Among the host of tropical American fringillines are the small finches known appropriately as seedeaters. The genus *Sporophila* contains some 30 species, ranging from southern Texas to Argentina. Tiny 4- to 5-inch birds with very short, heavy bills, seedeaters are common in grassy meadows, reedy marshes, and along roadsides and clearings, often in large, busy flocks. The males are black, marked with white or brown; the females dull brownish. The well known Black Seedeater is also called the Variable Seedeater because the male's markings are not constant.

Seedeaters are sociable birds and often nest fairly close together. They are not truly colonial in their nesting, but establish small territories and do not defend them avidly. The female builds a flimsy open cup nest near the ground, in a bush or low tree, and incubates the 2 to 3 eggs. The male feeds her while she incubates, and if she is absent when he comes bringing gifts he offers the food to the eggs.

YELLOW-FACED GRASSQUIT ♂
Tiaris olivacea
West Indies;
Mexico to Venezuela 4 in.

VARIABLE SEEDEATER ♂
Sporophila aurita
Mexico to Peru 4½ in.

SAFFRON FINCH ♂
Sicalis flaveola
Venezuela to Argentina;
Jamaica (intr.) 5½ in.

Seedeaters feed their young by regurgitation, bringing insects, small seeds, and grasses to the nest in their throats.

The Yellow-faced Grassquit is typical of four species of the genus *Tiaris* found from Mexico to Brazil. Similar in feeding and flocking habits to the *Sporophilas,* the grassquits are among the few continental small birds also found widely through the West Indies. Grassquits build covered nests with a thick roof and side entrance. The male helps with nest building, which is part of the courtship. He usually starts the nest and the female finishes it.

Domed nests are the custom of a few other tropical fringillines, notably some of the forest inhabitants of the genera *Arremon* and *Arremonops,* in which the sexes are closely alike, as in the Olive and Green-backed sparrows, and the Orange-billed Sparrow, whose bright beak, white throat and yellow wing markings are conspicuous recognition marks in the dark undergrowth these birds inhabit.

Most distinctive in nesting habits are the 10 ground finches of the genus *Sicalis* found in open brushlands from Mexico to Argentina, but most plentifully in southern South America, where they are called "wild canaries." Representative of these unusually bright fringillines is the Saffron Finch of South America, common in Jamaica where it was introduced. The Saffron Finches are one of the few cavity nesters in the family. They stuff a messy mass of straw and feathers into a hole in a tree, under the eaves of buildings, or in rock crevices. In southern Brazil they often appropriate abandoned domed nests of ovenbirds.

Classified as fringillines and not as richmondenines are the handsome Dominican and Crested cardinals. Residents of southern Brazil and Argentina, they are among the larger and gayer members of the subfamily. The Crested Cardinal has long been a popular cage bird, favored for its bright red crest and cheerful song. It has been introduced to Hawaii. Limited to the West Indies are several fringilline genera, notably the bullfinches of the genus *Loxigilla,* woodland species that build globular nests with side entrances.

The Old World component of the subfamily contains many common and familiar Eurasian birds. Widespread in Europe and eastern Asia is the Chaffinch, first of the family to be given a scientific name (*Fringilla*) by Linnaeus in 1758. By the inflexible rules of nomenclature this entire family of New World origin and essentially New World distribution derives its name from one of its Old World members.

The Chaffinch breeds throughout the European countryside and is a common summer resident in parks, gardens, thickets, hedgerows, and cultivated lands. Like most northern hemisphere members of the subfamily, it is gregarious when not nesting and migrates in flocks, often composed of one sex. It winters in open stubble fields with other seedeaters. The Brambling, a close relative, shares the genus *Fringilla* with it but is a more northern breeder, nesting in birch and conifer woodlands across northern Eurasia and migrating somewhat erratically southward, sometimes in tremendous numbers. One recent Brambling "invasion" that poured from the north into southern Germany and Switzerland was estimated to number in excess of 70 million birds.

The 30-odd species assigned to the species *Emberiza* and most commonly referred to as "buntings," are the largest single group of the Old World fringillines. Like most North American species, the emberizids are plain-colored birds with the sexes alike. Usually cryptically patterned in browns with streakings of black, white, and grays, many are attractively marked with yellow, and most have the outer tail feathers partly or wholly white. The genus has its greatest development across the Eurasian land mass, and most of its members are migratory or partly so.

Emberizid stock expanded successfully southward to invade the African home of the ploceids. The Golden-breasted Bunting lives throughout much of South Africa in open country, in sparse woodlands and cultivated areas, and is also a common resident in suburban gardens. Even more widespread is the Cape Bunting, found in many types of open country but partial to dry regions. It is often called the "rock bunting" because of its addiction to rocky hillside slopes. The Cape Bunting breaks into a number of geographical races over its wide range.

A representative emberizid is the Meadow Bunting of eastern Asia and Japan, an inhabitant of open fields, shrubby hillsides, and young second-growth woodland. It likes thickets along the roadsides and the hedgerows between cultivated fields. Meadow Buntings sing throughout the year, but most ardently in spring and summer. The male pipes his pleasant melody from the topmost twig of a bush, or from the electric wires along the country roads. As in the American Song Sparrow, each individual bird has his own particular melody and phraseology which he repeats over and over, sometimes for hours at a time.

Other well-known Eurasian species include the Pine, Cirl, Reed, and Little buntings. The Yellow Bunting, often called the yellowhammer, is one of the commonest finches in Great Britain. Nesting in the northern taiga from Sweden to Kamchatka is the Rustic Bunting, the only member of the genus admitted to the American list, as it occasionally straggles into the Aleutians. The Black-headed Bunting shown below is one of the more strikingly colored members of the group, and one of the few that lacks white in its outer tail feathers. The Corn Bunting, very common in the British Isles, also lacks the usual distinguishing mark of white in the outer tail feathers. This is one of the very few fringillines in which breeding aberrations are reported. Male Corn Buntings sometimes have as many as 4 or 5 mates.

The Ortolan of epicurean fame is one of the commoner

BRAMBLING ♂
Fringilla montifringilla
Northern Eurasia 6 in.

ORTOLAN BUNTING
Emberiza hortulana
Europe, western Asia 6½ in.

MEADOW BUNTING
Emberiza cioides
Turkestan to Japan 6 in.

BLACK-HEADED BUNTING
Emberiza melanocephala
Southeastern Europe,
southwestern Asia 6½ in.

European emberizids. Its name is probably a corruption of its scientific name *hortulana,* or gardener, for it is one of the common European garden residents. Ortolans gather in large flocks to migrate in the fall. Like most migrants, they take on quantities of fat for their long flight southward. For centuries Ortolans have been netted on their fall flight and served as a gourmet's tidbit. They are often kept in captivity and fattened further before they are marketed.

The nesting habits of the emberizine closely parallel those of the North American fringillines. All build open cup nests, sometimes in bushes or trees, seldom at any great height from the ground and often on it. Nest building and incubation are mainly by the female, though the male lends a hand in a few species. Clutches run from 3 to 6 eggs, usually 4 or 5, and most species are multibrooded. Eggs vary somewhat in color, but are typically lightly tinted and finely spotted.

OLD WORLD SEEDEATERS

PASSERIFORMES · PLOCEIDAE

The 375 or so seedeaters of Old World origin fall into three well-marked groups: the 112 goldfinches and allies (Carduelinae), the 107 waxbills (Estrildinae), and the 156 weaver finches, of which the nominate Ploceinae forms the largest of four closely allied subfamilies. The species within each of these three groups are closely related and share common ancestry, but that all three branched from the same parent stock is doubtful. While they share enough basic features to suggest some degree of kinship, many scholars now believe they arose from different stocks in different parts of the Eastern Hemisphere, and hence may each deserve family rank. The Ploceidae show no close ties to any other Old World

REDPOLL ♂
Acanthis flammea
Northern Northern Hemisphere.
Circumpolar 5½ in.

family, and we are still hoping to find fossil clues to their ancestry. Their closest similarities are to the New World seedeaters, for, as previously pointed out, the evolution of these two great avian complexes has been closely parallel. In addition to their stout, conical, seed-eating bills, the ploceids also show a reduction in the size of the outermost, or 10th, primary feather, though not so strongly as in their western counterparts. Many ploceids, the goldfinch subfamily in particular, retain a discernible 10th primary, which is usually less than half the length of the 9th. The feather has disappeared only in the most highly evolved types.

Other anatomical points of difference between the two families are manifest in the palate bones and jaw muscles. Rictal bristles, usually obvious in the New World seedeaters, are poorly developed and often absent in the ploceids. Two striking characteristics separating the families are the relative sizes of their legs and bills. In the Old World family the tarsus is relatively short, never longer than the middle toe with its claw. The exposed portion of the upper bill is relatively long, always more than twice the length of the gonys (the central ridge of the lower bill from its tip to the point of forking). The reverse is true for both these characteristics in the New World Fringillidae.

The goldfinches and their relatives in the subfamily Carduelinae are typified by the European Goldfinch, which feeds commonly on thistle seeds. Its generic name, bestowed on the subfamily, derives from the Latin *carduus,* a thistle. The carduelines are best developed in the Northern Hemisphere, and evidently originated in the Eurasian land mass we now call the palearctic region, where 64 species of 20 genera exist today. From this center the goldfinches have spread throughout Africa (30 species) and the Americas (32 species). Several species occur on all three continents. Three species have reached the East Indies and the Philippines, but none is known from Australia, or the Pacific islands.

With few exceptions the carduelines are tree-dwelling forest birds, much more so than the fringillines. All habitually sing during their peculiarly undulating flight, and their social instincts are highly developed. Few are strongly migratory, but most northern species move irregularly southward in winter. They travel in compactly unified flocks, and a number of species nest in loose colonies. Unlike the other ploceids, they build compactly woven, open cup nests, usually placed in tree branches well off the ground, except in the few species such as the redpolls that nest in treeless areas. Incubation is usually by the female alone, but the male feeds

HOUSE FINCH ♂
Carpodacus mexicanus
Western North America and Mexico 5½ in.

her on the nest and helps rear the young. A noteworthy aspect of their nesting habits which goldfinches share with the waxbills is their lack of nest sanitation. These are among the very few higher passerines that do not remove the nestlings' fecal matter from the nest.

Color and molt patterns vary throughout the carduelines. Some are streaked and mottled; others are clothed in solid hues. The sexes may be alike or different, and in many the males don a bright breeding dress of yellows or reds which they molt after breeding. In these species the winter males and first-year young resemble the females. In the European Goldfinch the sexes are alike the year round. In the congeneric American Goldfinch the sexes differ, and the male dons his bright-yellow and black breeding plumage in spring and doffs it in the late summer.

The European Goldfinch's neat beauty, its pleasant song, and the ease with which it is kept in captivity make it a popular cage bird, and thousands used to be caught for this purpose. A number of attempts were made to introduce the European Goldfinch to the United States during the 19th

BULLFINCH ♂
Pyrrhula pyrrhula
Temperate Eurasia   6 in.

WHITE-WINGED CROSSBILL ♂
Loxia leucoptera
Northern Hemisphere   5¾ in.

SISKIN ♂
Carduelis spinus
North temperate Eurasia   5 in.

EUROPEAN GOLDFINCH ♂
Carduelis carduelis
Europe, western Asia, northwest Africa   5¼

century, and releases were made in Oregon, Missouri, Ohio, New Jersey, and Massachusetts, as well as in Bermuda. Though small populations still persist in favored spots along the south shore of Long Island, the species found conditions to its liking only in Bermuda, where it is now one of the common resident birds. It has also been introduced in Australia and New Zealand.

Close relatives of the goldfinches are the European Twite and Linnet, and the northernmost members of the family, the circumpolar redpolls that breed in the arctic tundra the world around and migrate southward in winter to temperate latitudes. Widest ranging of the subfamily are the 22 very similar yellowish siskins found in coniferous and deciduous woodlands throughout the Northern Hemisphere. Siskins have acclimatized themselves southward in Africa to the Cape of Good Hope, and have followed the American cordilleras to the Straits of Magellan. They are the only carduelines in South America. One siskin has been isolated in the coniferous mountain forests of Hispaniola long enough to become generically distinct. The only other strictly American genus of carduelines is the strong-billed Evening Grosbeak of northern forests, which flocks irregularly in winter and often comes to window-box feeding stations in the northern states for sunflower seeds.

Prominent among the reddish-colored carduelines is the Purple Finch of North America, replaced in Eurasia by the Scarlet Finch and several rose finches, all of the genus *Carpodacus*. Very similar to the Purple Finch is the slightly smaller and brighter Mexican House Finch, a common dooryard bird from California southward through Mexico. In 1940 cage-bird dealers in southern California shipped numbers of these birds, caught illegally in the wild, to New York dealers for sale as "Hollywood finches." Alert agents of the Fish and Wildlife Service spotted this violation of the International Migratory Bird Treaty Act and quickly put an end to the traffic. To avoid prosecution the New York dealers released their birds. The species was soon noted in the wild

RED AVADAVAT ♂
Estrilda amandava
India to Indochina
and East Indies   3 in.

BLUE-FACED ♂
PARROT FINCH
Erythrura trichroa
Micronesia to New Ireland
and New Hebrides   4½ in.

CHESTNUT MANNIKIN ♂
Lonchura ferruginosa
India to Philippines and East Indies   4¾ in.

on nearby Long Island, and it has slowly been increasing its range ever since. The Mexican House Finch has now pushed northward into Connecticut and southward into New Jersey. It has also been introduced to Hawaii.

One of the largest carduelines is the 9-inch Pine Grosbeak. The male is dull red, the female grayish brown with a yellowish crown and rump. The Pine Grosbeak breeds circumpolarly in the pine-spruce belt across northern North America and Eurasia, wintering irregularly southward. Similarly distributed are the Red and the White-winged crossbills. Both males are ruddy, both females brownish. The crossbills' strong bill with uniquely overlapped tips is an ideal tool for prying seeds out of tough evergreen cones, and the birds are seldom found far from conifers. They do eat other seeds, and they feed their young on insects. Crossbills have pushed southward following the evergreens in both hemispheres. A population of Red Crossbills inhabits the Central American highlands from Guatemala to Nicaragua. A wandering group of White-winged Crossbills that reached Hispaniola still lives there with the endemic siskin in the highland conifer forests.

Well-known Eurasian carduelines include the Hawfinch of Europe, a husky-bodied bird named for its fondness for the seeds of the hawthorn. In eastern Asia, the Hawfinch is replaced by the 9-inch Japanese Grosbeak. Found across Eurasia are 10 geographical races of the Bullfinch, which is admitted to the American list on the basis of straggling records in Alaska. The Bullfinch is popular as a cage bird in Europe and the Orient, and is prized for the lovely pink color of the male's breast and for its sweet piping calls.

The best known of all cage birds, the Canary, is a cardueline finch of the siskin type. Wild Canaries still exist on the Canary Islands, whence they were imported into Europe as cage birds in the 16th century. They live on the Azores and Madeira islands as well. Other relatives of the same genus occur in Africa and Europe, best known of which is the Serin. The wild Canary stock is olivish above streaked with brown and black, and greenish yellow below. Centuries of selective breeding in captivity both for color and for song and crossing with closely related species have produced the many distinctive varieties now available.

The second subfamily of Old World seedeaters, the Estrildinae, are also great favorites among cage-bird fanciers. The appeal of the waxbills to aviculturists is their bright colors, spritely liveliness, and ready adaptability to confinement. They are poor singers, and though some males have pleasant warbling notes, most of them are limited to simple chirps, hisses, buzzes, and subdued chatterings. Members of this kaleidoscopic group are known to the trade by such fanciful and descriptive names as mannikins, munias, parrotfinches, negrofinches, firefinches, locustfinches, crimsonwings, cutthroats, silvereyes, bluebills, cordon-bleus, and grenadiers, to mention but a few.

RED-CHEEKED CORDON-BLEU ♂
Uraeginthus bengalensis
Africa, Senegal to the Sudan 4½ in.

GREEN TIGER FINCH ♂
Estrilda formosa
Central India 4 in.

GOULDIAN FINCH ♂
Poephila gouldiae
Northern Australia 5¾ in.

MELBA FINCH ♂
Pytelia melba
Central and southern Africa 5 in.

Despite their great diversity of colors, the estrildids are a remarkably uniform group anatomically and in habits and behavior. Native to the tropical parts of the Old World, Africa, southern Asia, the East Indies, and Australia, the 107 species are divided among 15 genera. All are very small birds, 6 inches in length at most, with short, stout, pointed bills. They are nonmigratory and generally resident wherever they occur. They favor open grasslands, reedy marshes, or the brushy borders of forest edges and clearings. All are ground feeders that live mainly on the small seeds of grasses and sedges, augmented by a few insects and an occasional small fruit or berry.

The waxbills are highly gregarious and customarily go about in flocks, sometimes of tremendous size, often containing 3 or 4 species. Many of them nest colonially. All build large domed nests, globular, melon-, pear-, or bottle-shaped, but notably flimsy and of loose construction, and with side entrances. A number of them build separate nests for roosting. They lay large clutches of from 4 to 10 pure-white eggs. Both sexes build the nest and care for the young,

YELLOW-BELLIED WAXBILL ♂
Estrilda melanotis
South Africa   4 in.

GREEN-BACKED TWINSPOT ♂
Estrilda nitidula
South Africa   3 in.

LOCUST FINCH ♂
Estrilda locustella
Southeast Africa, Tanganyika   3½ in.

and the male usually helps to some extent with the incubation, which runs from 11 to 17 days. While waxbills do not remove their nestlings' droppings, these always dry up quickly, crumble away, and do not foul the nest excessively. The nestlings have bright patches of color inside the mouths, the sight of which is thought to stimulate the parent's feeding reactions. The young mature rapidly and are able to breed in their first year.

The nominate genus *Estrilda* contains 28 species ranging from Africa to Australia. Typical of the genus is the Common Waxbill, found over most of Africa south of the Sahara in reedy marshes. The Yellow-bellied Waxbill lives in small flocks along forest edges or in thick tangles of underbrush bordering streams. The tiny Locust Finches move about wet grasslands in dense swarms, and are almost impossible to see when feeding on the ground. When disturbed they rise and fly straight and fast with rapidly whirring wings and drop quickly again into concealment in the grass.

Other African species are the Green-backed Twinspot, which eats termites as well as grass seeds, and the Orange-

WHITE-HEADED BUFFALO WEAVER ♂
Dinamellia dinamelli
Sedan and Abyssinia to Kenya 9 in.

**RED-BILLED
QUELEA** ♂
Quelea quelea
Africa south
of the Sahara 5 in.

HOUSE SPARROW ♂
Passer domesticus
Eurasia, North
Africa 6 in.

**EURASIAN
TREE SPARROW**
Passer montanus
Eurasia 5½ in.

cheeked Waxbill, which has become established in Puerto Rico from escaped cage birds. Other favorite cage birds are the several cordon-bleus, common around villages and cultivated lands in East Africa. The cordon-bleus often build their domed nests near those of wasps for protection, and occasionally use the abandoned nests of weaverbirds, relining them with feathers and plant down. The three species of red-faced melba finches are inconspicuous inhabitants of thorny thickets and undergrowth, where they search about quietly on the ground for small seeds.

A brilliant little Asiatic estrildid is the Red Avadavat (a corruption of Ahmadabad, the Indian city from which the first were sent to Europe). Avadavats live in dense swarms in reedy marshes and wet grasslands. They nest irregularly throughout the year, but most often in the rainy season, when food is plentiful. Netted in quantity for the live-bird trade, they become tame and confiding in captivity.

The 30 munias and mannikins of the genus *Lonchura*, found from Africa across southern Asia to the Caroline Islands and southward to Australia, are one of the largest groups of estrildids. Most of them are reddish brown, variously patterned with black and white. They are grassland birds of savannas and reedy marshes. These prolific little birds lay 4 to 8 eggs and in captivity rear up to 5 broods a year. The young breed before they are a year old.

Mannikins often congregate in swarms in grain fields. The Chestnut Mannikin is one of the main pests of rice growers in the Philippines and Malaya. Flocks of Bronze Mannikins traipse about the open lands of the Congo following the food supply as grasses and grains ripen. Bronze Mannikins roost communally, jammed in on top of one another in old nests and in special nests they build for sleeping. One of the brighter members of this group is the Java Sparrow, common in bird shops where it is sold as a cage bird. This chunky gray bird tinged with pink on the belly has two large white ear patches and a light-pink bill. It makes an attractive pet, but its presence in rice fields is not relished by farmers. Its fitting scientific name is *Padda oryzivora,* which means the paddy-field rice-eater.

Limited to the Australian and Oriental region are 23 species of colorful grass-finches or parrot-finches divided among three genera. Typical of the nine species of the genus *Poephila,* known in northern Australia as painted finches or purple-breasted finches, is the gaudy Gouldian Finch. Gouldian Finches have the tail pointed instead of square, and live in small flocks in open grassy country, often near watercourses. A close relative and a common Australian bird is the Zebra Finch, often seen in cages, with its zebra-barred black and white tail, chestnut ear patches, and pink bill. These finches build bottle-shaped nests of dried grasses in a bush or low tree, sometimes in tall grass, and occasionally in tree hollows, an unusual departure in this subfamily.

Also with pointed tails are the nine parrot-finches (*Erythrura*), bright green in color with contrasting reds and blues. Most of them live along forest edges, and they are frequently found in bamboo tangles, where their green colors are very hard to see. A widespread member of this genus is the Blue-faced, or Three-colored, Parrot-finch, a resident of many Pacific islands from the Solomons, New Hebrides, and Loyalty Islands, northward to the Carolines and westward to the Bismarck Archipelago. Others occur in the Philippines, Malaya, Papua, and northern Australia.

The third assemblage of Old World seedeaters, the weaver-birds, is composed of four subfamilies, the buffalo weavers (Bubalornithinae), the sparrow weavers (Passerinae), the typical weavers (Ploceinae), and the widow weavers (Viduinae). The weavers have by far their greatest development in Africa, where the group arose. From here members of two subfamilies have pushed widely through the palearctic and the fringes of the oriental region, and one of the sparrow weavers, the ubiquitous House Sparrow, has, with the help of man, become perhaps the most widely distributed and familiar small bird in the world.

Though a few species are solitary, most weavers are highly

gregarious, and some have brought social development to its highest point in the bird kingdom. They are named for the highly complex nests many of them weave, some of which are tremendous communal structures. Others do not weave at all, but build crude, clumsy conglomerations of sticks and straws. One group, the widow weavers, are social parasites and build no nest. The sex life of many weavers is highly involved. They have intricate courtship patterns, and polygamy is common throughout the group.

Though few weavers have well-developed songs, most are quite noisy. Their calls are simple chirps and chatterings. Their voices tend to be harsh and monotonous. Essentially sedentary birds, few weavers have developed regular migration patterns. Many wander widely in search of food, and some shift their breeding grounds seasonally or from year to year. Though usually found in open country, they occupy many types of habitat. A very few live in deep forests; some like open woodlands, others rocky hillsides; many dwell in savannas, grasslands, or marshes. A number of them, the House Sparrow in particular, have tied their destinies to man and live most successfully around human habitations.

The most primitive and uniform group are the three buffalo weavers. These large, stocky African sparrows are 8 to 10 inches long, two of them dressed in somber blacks and browns, the third with a white head and underparts. Buffalo weavers roam the dry savannas and veldts in small flocks of a dozen or so, feeding on the ground about equally on insects and grass seeds. They build bulky compartmented nests of sticks heaped together on the branches of large trees, and strew thorny twigs along the supporting limbs to discourage climbing marauders. They may build 8 or 10 nests in the same tree, each nest with two or more inner chambers occupied by separate pairs and with separate entrances facing outward in different directions.

Prominent among the 35 sparrow weavers is the House Sparrow, whose generic name *Passer,* Latin for sparrow, is bestowed on the entire order of perching birds. Native to

Europe, western Asia, and northern Africa, the House Sparrow is the most successful city and town dweller of all birds, and has followed European civilization all over the world. It was introduced to North America in 1852 (in a Brooklyn, N.Y., cemetery), and its subsequent spread throughout the settled parts of the continent is now practically complete. It has been almost equally successful in South Africa, South America, Australia, New Zealand, and Hawaii. A few introductions have failed. House Sparrows were unable to survive in southern Greenland, which is not surprising. In the Philippines they were unable to compete with their close relative, the Eurasian Tree Sparrow (not to be confused with the nearctic fringilline of the same common name, p. 289), which had already been introduced there from Asia and occupies the same niche around villages.

The Eurasian Tree Sparrow closely resembles the male House Sparrow, and the sexes are alike. Widsepread in cultivated regions from central Europe eastward to China, Korea, and Japan, this species is just as ubiquitous around towns as the House Sparrow, and a great nuisance in rice-growing regions. Tremendous flocks descend on the paddies as the rice ripens in the fall, and all sorts of scarecrows, noisemakers, and smoke bombs are used to discourage them—with little effect. The Japanese net them by the millions—between 5 and 10 million are sold annually. Their plucked bodies hang in the markets, their necks inserted in twists of rice-straw rope in skeins of 10 each. In season they are a common delicacy at Oriental dinners, and in Tokyo little street-side stalls sell them broiled on skewers over charcoal and flavored with soy sauce. Broiled to a crisp and eaten bones and all, they are quite tasty. A small population of Eurasian Tree Sparrows is resident around St. Louis, Missouri. They were introduced there in 1870 but have never spread.

Close to the *Passer* group is the Snow Finch (*Montifringilla*) of the southern Eurasian mountains. The Snow Finch nests above 4,500 feet in the Pyrenees, Alps, Apennines, and the Balkans, and up to 16,000 feet in the Himalayas. Familiar to mountain climbers and common about Alpine hostels, the Snow Finch looks like a female House Sparrow with large patches of white in its wings. Another allied group is the rock sparrows (*Petronia*), found on dry rocky slopes and semideserts from South Africa northward to southern Europe and the Himalayas.

These sparrow weavers build untidy bulky nests, always domed with a side entrance when out in the open. More frequently the House Sparrow and its close kin appropriate a crevice among rocks or a hole in a tree or building which they fill with a mass of straw, twigs, feathers, and trash. The House and Tree sparrows frequently nest under house eaves wherever they can jam a cranny with nesting material. The House Sparrow lays 4 to 9 white eggs heavily speckled with gray which the female incubates practically alone. The incubation and fledging periods each average 13 to 14 days, and two or more broods are raised annually.

Most specialized of the sparrow weavers is the Social Weaver of South Africa, whose large communal nests are sometimes mistaken at a distance for native huts. From 100 to 300 pairs of Social Weavers pool their efforts to build their apartment dwelling, which may be 10 feet high and 15 feet in diameter, usually high in the branches of a sturdy tree, preferably one standing by itself in the open. The birds start by building the communal roof, a waterproof canopy of straw thatch. Hanging from its underside, each pair weaves its own retort-shaped nest chamber, entered by a tube woven from the bottom. Sparrow Weavers nest in the South African midsummer, around Christmas time. Each pair lays 2 to 4 dull-white eggs heavily speckled with dark gray. Each flock remains about its nest tree throughout the year, chattering to one another continually (they have no true song). When not nesting they forage in small flocks for grass seeds and insects, and return at night to roost in the shelter of their dwelling.

The typical weavers of the subfamily Ploceinae number about 109 species, most of them African, a few in southern

Asia. In most of this group the sexes are unlike. The dull-brown females resemble female House Sparrows, while the males in breeding dress are usually bright with yellow and black. After the breeding season the males don an "eclipse" dress much like that of the female. The young resemble the female throughout the first year, and do not mature into breeding dress until the end of their second year. A few nest solitarily, but most are highly social and nest in colonies which run from a few pairs to millions. All weave beautiful flasklike or retort-shaped nests, with the entrance either at the side or through a long tube from the bottom.

Representative of the Ploceinae is the Village Weaver, a common resident around native settlements throughout much of Africa. Large isolated trees may contain hundreds of their nests, which are not united into a single structure as with the Social Weaver, but are built separately, each on its own twig or branch. The male bird starts the nest by weaving a frame of palm fibers, obtained by nipping a small slit in the palm frond and tearing off a long strip by flying away with it in his beak. On the framework he weaves an inverted flask, entered through a funnel from the bottom. The female finishes the nest by lining it with softer material. Though in some colonies the sexes are about in balance, there is often an excess of females. When a male has one female safely ensconced on her eggs, he usually starts a new nest at once for another mate.

A similar Asiatic species is the Baya Weaver, an exceedingly common bird in India, Indochina, and Malaya. Its flask nests hang in colonies of 8 or 10, sometimes 50 or 100, from the trees in rural villages. As with the Village Weaver, the male Baya starts the nest, weaving a firm support of grass fibers around a branch, from which he braids a hanging loop. To the loop he weaves thick walls, and adds a hollow tube for access down one side. This varies in length from a few inches to several feet. When the outside of the nest is complete, the hens begin to appear at the colony, and each makes her choice of the structures built by the males. When

1 SOCIAL WEAVER ♂
Philetairus socius
South Africa   5½ in.

**2 PARADISE
WIDOWBIRD** ♂
Steganura paradisaea
Tropical Africa   15 in.

3 RED BISHOP ♂
Pyromelana orix
South Africa   5½ in.

4 VILLAGE ♂
(BLACK-HEADED) WEAVER
Ploceus cucullatus
Eritrea and Abyssinia   6 in.

5 SPECTACLED WEAVER ♂
Hyphanturgus ocularis
Tropical Africa   6½ in.

she finds one to her liking, the hen finishes off the interior with softer materials while the male completes the outside tube. As soon as she has laid her eggs and started incubating, the male Baya starts a new nest. The polygamous males keep on building nests throughout the season and, except where there is a substantial surplus of females, are often left with unfinished and unoccupied nests.

Several African members of this group have become serious economic pests in agricultural areas. The worst of these is the Red-billed Quelea, a little 5-inch grayish-brown bird with a bright red bill. The male has red markings around the head and a black mask in the breeding season, but at other times it resembles the duller sparrowlike female. Queleas wander about aimlessly in tremendous swarms in the open and semiwooded savanna country, and when one of these flocks, which may number into the millions, visits crop lands as the grain is ripening, their depredations are so enormous that they have been combated with flame throwers and chemicals spread from aircraft.

The highly prolific Queleas are opportunist nesters and, unlike most other weavers, they are able to breed when they are one year old. Their breeding is triggered by the rainy season and, when conditions are propitious, the birds settle down together to the business of reproduction wherever they happen to be. The great flocks seem to pick fresh breeding grounds every year. These sometimes cover hundreds of acres, every tree of which is festooned with their nests. The males build the nests, which are simple oval structures woven of strips of grass with little or no lining and an entrance at one side near the top. As soon as a nest is finished and the female accepts it, pairing takes place and the eggs are laid within the next day or two. In these mass nestings there seems to be little polygamy, for the male shares some of the incubating duties during the day, the female always incubating at night. The young hatch in 13 days, usually all at once throughout the colony. They leave the nest in another 12 days, and the large flocks are soon on their erratically wandering way again, augmented by the many young.

The most ornamental members of this group are the bishop and whidah weavers. The male Red Bishop is one of the brightest-colored of all the weavers and has one of the most interesting courtships. He displays in a bouncing flight before his harem of 2 or 3 females, and makes clapping noises with his wings. Bishops nest in reed beds and wet marshes, building an oval shell of a nest slung between upright reeds. Bishops are great termite eaters, but the large flocks often damage crops, and African farmers are not infrequently put to considerable expense keeping them away from their ripening grain.

A closely related group are sometimes called widows, but more properly whidahs (an anglicization of Ouidah, the coastal town on the Gulf of Guinea where the first of them were obtained). These are also small-bodied birds. The males in breeding season are not only bedecked with gay colors but often with long tail feathers. The male Long-tailed Whidah, a shining black bird with scarlet wing patches, is the longest bird in the family, just under 2 feet in length despite its small body. The courting male Jackson's Whidah builds himself a dancing ground reminiscent of those of the bowerbirds. He clears a round arena 4 feet or so in diameter in the grassy veldt, leaving a single column of grass untouched in the center. Around this he jumps and prances and spreads his tail in a manner which females of his species apparently find irresistible. Whidah weavers are strongly polygynous; each male has a harem of 4 to 12 plain-colored hens, which nest in groups on the grassy veldt. During the day the male goes from one nest to another encouraging the females with churring notes. At evening he leaves with his long tail streaming behind him to roost in the reeds with other males.

The strangest and most aberrant of all the weavers are nine species of the subfamily Viduinae, the true widowbirds. These birds of open grasslands and savannas are widespread throughout Africa south of the Sahara. The females are inconspicuous brown birds, but the males in breeding dress with their long fancy tails are among the most striking of all the seedeaters.

All the widowbirds are both polygynous and parasitic, and with these sexual abnormalities have developed intricate courtship displays. Some of these long-tailed weavers make extended courtship flights. Rising 200 to 300 feet into the air, they hover a few moments with flapping wings and waving tail. Then they coast down to the female in the grass below, trusting these antics have entranced her into a state of receptiveness.

In their parasitism the widowbirds are highly selective in their choice of hosts. They lay their eggs chiefly in the nests of certain waxbill finches, each species of widowbird parasitizing only one or a few species of waxbill. Their eggs, instead of being tinted or spotted as in all other weavers, are pure white like those of their estrildine hosts. Even more amazing, the nestling parasites have bright mouth markings similar to those of their hosts. This phenomenon probably stems from the common ancestry of the two groups.

The female widowbird is believed in some cases to remove an egg from her host's nest, but otherwise this parasitism is apparently not unduly harmful to the waxbills. The dupes rear the young widowbirds with their own broods, and the foster fledgling gets along well with its nestmates, which it closely resembles. It would be interesting to know just when and how young widowbirds, conditioned by and "imprinted" to foster parents, suddenly realize they are birds of a different feather and leave to find others of their own kind. We have much to learn about social parasitism, not only in these weavers, but in the cuckoos, honeyguides, and cowbirds that also practice it successfully.

INDEX

SCARLET-BACKED FLOWERPECKER ♂
Dicaeum cruentatum
India to southern China and East Indies   3½ in.
Text reference on page 234